TECHNICAL ILLUSTRATING

TECHNICAL
ILLUSTRATING

A. EDWARD HARVEY

A.R.C.A. L.R.I.B.A. M.S.I.A.
M.Inst.R.A. N.R.D.

LONDON

B. T. BATSFORD LTD

First published, 1960

© A. Edward Harvey, 1960

MADE AND PRINTED IN GREAT BRITAIN
BY WILLIAM CLOWES AND SONS, LIMITED, LONDON AND BECCLES
FOR THE PUBLISHERS

B. T. BATSFORD LTD
4 FITZHARDINGE STREET, PORTMAN SQUARE, W.1

PREFACE

This book has been planned as a standard work of reference in the art of drawing for technical illustration, i.e. the technique of producing pictorial line and wash illustrations including exploded and cut-away views by projection from workshop drawings. Therefore its ingredients are, as far as possible, of a timeless quality, based on established practice—not on conjecture or ephemeral conditions. It contains only factual truths concerning a subject which has become of tremendous importance to industry—particularly to aircraft and motor car organisations. It is a distillation of fundamental principles and facts and a study of their application by twenty-two organisations—ranging from ministries to firms with international reputations—with well-documented case histories.

The reader is offered for the first time facilities to become familiar, not only with theory, but with unique examples of professional practice ranging from components to the most complex industrial projects.

From personal experience, both as a teacher and as a practitioner, I know the problems which must be solved, the difficulties to be overcome and the degree of proficiency expected if the young artist is to achieve not only success but also that self-confidence which, in my opinion, should be regarded as an essential part of his equipment.

By intensive, carefully planned study, and by methods practical as well as theoretical, the reader is initiated into the practice of technical illustrating. Sections 1 and 2 deal cogently with orthographic projection and conventional three-dimensional space projections which must be understood, not only by the technical draughtsman, but also by the illustrator who often has to create three-dimensional technical illustrations of projects still in the blue-print stage. The reader who requires more detailed information on the fundamentals is advised to study *Trade Draughtsmanship* by the present author and published by B. T. Batsford Ltd. This work and the present volume cover fully the graphic requirements of the syllabus for the Intermediate and Final Examinations in Technical Illustration of the City and Guilds of London Institute.

Finally, I am most grateful to the directors and executives of ministries, corporations and business organisations who responded magnificently to my requests for co-operation so that this work should adequately represent the best of contemporary technical illustrating.

PREFACE

The final choice was extremely onerous as I had a veritable *embarras de richesses* for my consideration. Without their willing and helpful co-operation this work would have lacked the visual evidence of the high standard of ability expected of the professional artist.

Cheltenham 1960   A.E.H.

CONTENTS

CONTENTS

ACKNOWLEDGMENT

Acknowledgment is due to the following for permission to reproduce in this work illustrations which are copyright and also for their kind and whole-hearted co-operation in many ways:

Associated Electrical Industries Limited (A.E.I.), 33 Grosvenor Place, London, S.W.1.

Associated Equipment Company (A.E.C.) Limited, Southall, Middlesex.

The British Motor Corporation Limited (The Austin Motor Company Limited), Longbridge, Birmingham.

Bristol Aircraft Limited, Filton House, Bristol.

British Olivetti Ltd, 30 Berkeley Square, London, W.1.

Crown Copyright—Controller of H.M. Stationery Office (Ministry of Aviation, Savoy Hill House, London, W.C.2).

Directorate General of Equipment (Air Ministry, Harrogate, Yorkshire).

Electrolux Limited, Electrolux Works, Luton, Beds.

Fairey Aviation Limited, Hayes, Middlesex.

Ford Motor Company Ltd, Dagenham, Essex.

Hawker Aircraft Ltd, Richmond Road, Kingston-upon-Thames, Surrey.

High Precision Equipment Ltd, Bletchley, Bucks.

Ideal-Standard Ideal Boilers & Radiators Ltd, Ideal House, Great Marlborough Street, London, W.1.

Imperial Chemical Industries Limited (I.C.I.), Plastics Division, Black Fan Road, Welwyn Garden City, Herts.

The Kleine Company Ltd, 9–13 George Street, Manchester Square, London, W.1.

Marconi's Wireless Telegraph Company Limited, Aeronautical Division, Marconi House, Chelmsford, Essex.

The Mavitta Drafting Machines Ltd, Highlands Road, Shirley, Solihull, Warwickshire.

Principal Reginald Brill, Kingston School of Art, Kingston-upon-Thames, Surrey.

ix

ACKNOWLEDGMENT

Rolls-Royce Limited, Aero Engine Division, Derby.

Standard-Triumph Sales Ltd, Capmartin Road, Radford, Coventry.

United Kingdom Atomic Energy Authority, Atomic Energy Research Establishment, Harwell, Didcot, Berks.

Vauxhall Motors Limited, Luton, Beds.

Introduction

A thorough practical training in drawing offices actively engaged in production, coupled with sound theoretical knowledge of the basic techniques of draughtsmanship and principles of projection as propounded in the author's previous work *Trade Draughtsmanship* (B. T. Batsford Ltd) and their application in the present work, is essential for achieving success as a Technical Illustrator.

The technical illustrator is often a specialist whose work falls squarely between the two extremes of draughtsmanship as understood, on the one hand, by the commercial artist, and on the other hand, by the engineering or architectural draughtsman, although in some offices many draughtsmen are also capable illustrators.

Both the engineering and architectural draughtsman work to established rules and formulae, the idiom or grammar being a kind of technical language, intelligible to technicians in these professions but not necessarily so to the layman.

Conversely, the technical illustrator by his knowledge and technique produces the explanatory drawing in its various forms as an intelligible interpreter of fact which will give practically all the answers sought by the uninitiated as well as by the initiated.

There are several kinds of explanatory drawing and the choice depends upon the type of intelligence they are intended to impart:

First, illustrative perspective drawings presenting the actual appearance in readily understandable form, ranging from a designer's 'doodles' to highly rendered worked perspectives.

Second, the graphic representation of the sectionised object revealing parts of the exterior surface and slicing into the object to show the construction of the inside, i.e., the cut-away view and/or the sectioned drawing.

Third, the exploded view of the object in which the components are taken apart, and placed on the axis of rotation so that compression along this axis would result in reassembly.

Aviation companies and the motor corporations in particular, attach the greatest importance to technical illustrating. To meet the needs of normal or expanding programmes for development projects, for design and for research work, opportunities of exceptional scope exist for designer-draughtsmen and technical illustrators. But they must have

1

a comprehensive knowledge of these three pictorial means of communicating mechanical and design intelligence, as well as great skill and patience for the exacting qualities of draughtsmanship needed.

Standardisation: an attempt is being made to standardise the presentation of technical information in the aircraft industry. This, of course, includes the standard and format of illustrations.

The proposed scheme has been prepared for the Air Transport Association of America and is available in draft form known as *Specification for Manufacturers' Technical Data ATA Specification No. 100.*

Almost every manufacturer is inclined to believe that the breadth of art school training is insufficient to meet the practical needs peculiar to his industry and many prefer to recruit their draughtsmen and technical illustrators from within the organisation. The prejudice is often born of the bitter experience of discovering that the applicants' paper qualifications seldom reveal, in practice, sufficient knowledge of technique, method and routine, therefore the process of learning has to begin all over again.

It is natural enough in such circumstances that industry should prefer to educate their future artists on an apprenticeship basis so that there is a pool of artists available. It will be appreciated that this system can deny the student the opportunity to study in a different atmosphere drawing and graphic art as well as acquiring an academic background. Nevertheless, from the manufacturers' standpoint, this is more than offset by the asset of practical ability, which to them is the economic course to pursue and the one which pays dividends.

Facilities in certain technical colleges and colleges of art do exist, particularly day-release and evening courses for those already in drawing offices. The teachers, often professional illustrators, in those schools with first-rate graphic art departments, have part-time courses intended to prepare students for the Intermediate and Final Examinations of the City and Guilds of London Institute. The normal duration of the course is five years; the first three lead to the Intermediate, the remaining two to the Final Examination; in certain cases applicants over 25 years of age may enter the final years of the course and the Final Examination direct. Full syllabuses and conditions of entry are shown in the Institute's *Regulations and Syllabus for Printing Subjects.* This work on *Technical Illustrating* and the author's *Trade Draughtsmanship* published by B. T. Batsford Ltd, deal comprehensively with the graphic requirements for these two important examinations.

SECTION I

Technical Drawing: A

ORTHOGRAPHIC PROJECTION

The technical illustration is the visual explanation of the design for a machine, a product or even a nuclear installation. For industrial production, drawings must be made which will show accurately the shape and measurements of the proposed project before it can be manufactured or built. Working drawings true to scale are made from the designer's drawings in such a manner that the engineers or others who are responsible for the actual floor production know exactly what is planned.

The only method of conveying these intentions without ambiguity is by drawings in orthographic projection, i.e. by plans, elevations and sections. Illustration 1 shows in isometric projection (one of the conventional three-dimensional space projections which will be explained on pp. 7 and 9), two abstract solids of similar shape in first angle and third angle projection respectively. For practical purposes the first and third quadrants only are used for projection; in the second and fourth quadrants the views are difficult to plot and cause confusion. Projection in the first quadrant is the original system and was at one time universal. It is still current practice in Europe and to a larger extent in Great Britain, but in North America projection in the third quadrant is the habitual practice. The British Standards Institution permits both systems as British Standards.

In both cases we assume that the object to be drawn is suspended in space, i.e. in the angle between two vertical planes and a horizontal plane known as the planes of projection. Note: For demonstration purposes the model of the four quadrants is assumed to be of transparent perspex as the first angle projection overlaps the third angle projection in the isometric view.

I The Principle of First Angle or English Projection

The object is imagined as suspended in the angle made by the two vertical planes (i.e. the front plane and the side plane) and the horizontal plane. The top or plan of the object is obtained by lines projected downwards on to the horizontal plane; the end farthest from the side vertical plane is projected on to this plane, and is called the side or end elevation; finally the front is projected on to the front vertical plane and is called the front elevation. [The three black arrows clearly indicate the appropriate directions.]

The diagram in the top left-hand corner shows that in practice the draughtsman imagines the planes hinged and opened out flat. Professionally this relationship is known as English Projection with its three basic rules:

    (i) All elevations are projected horizontally, one from the other.

    (ii) An end or side elevation is projected to the opposite side of the front elevation.

    (iii) The top or plan is projected and drawn directly below the front elevation.

2 The Principle of Third Angle or American Projection

Again in this case the object is imagined as suspended in the angle made by the two vertical planes and the horizontal plane, but this time it is above the vertical planes. The draughtsman in looking through the transparent planes sees the face of the object nearest to the plane. Therefore as the horizontal plane is above the vertical planes the plan is obtained by lines projected vertically upwards on to it. Front and end elevations are obtained by projecting lines horizontally on to the respective vertical planes. [The three black arrows clearly indicate the appropriate directions.]

The diagram in the bottom right-hand corner again shows in practice the hinged planes opened out flat, but as the horizontal plane is above the vertical planes this is swung upwards. Professionally this relationship is known as American Projection with its three basic rules:

    (i) All the elevations are projected horizontally, one from the other.

    (ii) An end or side elevation is projected to the same side of the front elevation as the end or side which is being drawn.

    (iii) The top or plan is projected and drawn directly above the elevations.

Both English and American projection methods are explained because some industrial organisations have adopted the latter in spite of the former being the traditional system in this country. To avoid confusion state clearly the method used in large type at the top of the drawing, preferably on the centre line.

It is fairly common practice for technical illustrators to be called upon to produce graphic sectionised views and exploded drawings from blue prints at a very early stage of development. In certain engineering drawing offices many draughtsmen are expected to be equally proficient at orthographic projections and at all the conventional three-dimensional projections.

4

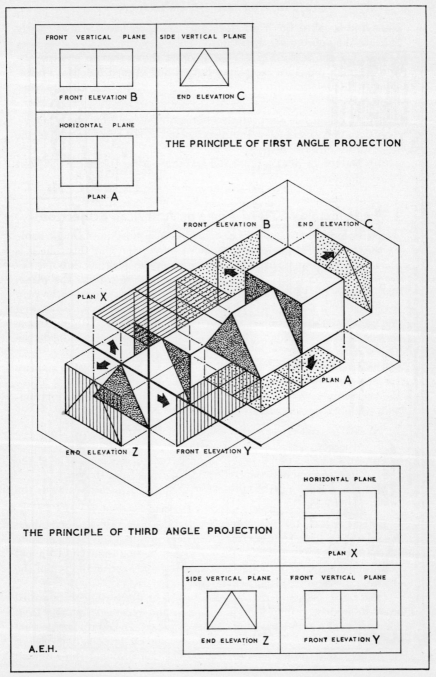

FRONT VERTICAL PLANE

SIDE VERTICAL PLANE

FRONT ELEVATION B

END ELEVATION C

HORIZONTAL PLANE

THE PRINCIPLE OF FIRST ANGLE PROJECTION

PLAN A

FRONT ELEVATION B   END ELEVATION C

PLAN X

PLAN A

END ELEVATION Z   FRONT ELEVATION Y

THE PRINCIPLE OF THIRD ANGLE PROJECTION

HORIZONTAL PLANE

PLAN X

SIDE VERTICAL PLANE   FRONT VERTICAL PLANE

END ELEVATION Z   FRONT ELEVATION Y

A.E.H.

1 The principles of first angle/English projection and third angle/American projection

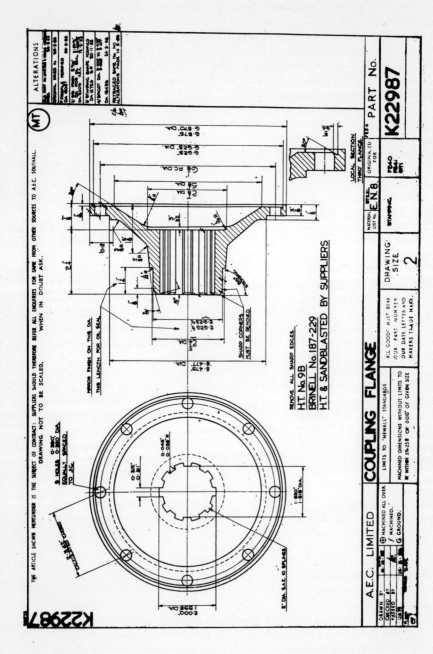

2 A.E.C. Ltd. Typical workshop line drawing (orthographic projection)

The blue print (Illustration 2) is typical of top-grade engineering draughtsmanship. Nothing has been left to chance and it even carries the caption 'when in doubt ask'. It is from such an orthographic drawing as this that technical illustrations are made. Section 1 of *Trade Draughtsmanship* which analyses the principles of drawing office procedure gives all the techniques for producing drawings of this type for those readers who require detailed advice.

Outline drawings in orthographic projection invariably preface manufacturers' workshop manuals, particularly those issued by the service divisions of the aircraft, motorcar and engineering industries. These drawings are produced by illustrators.

Technical Drawing: B

CONVENTIONAL THREE-DIMENSIONAL SPACE PROJECTIONS

The technical illustration is the graphic explanation of a designer's conception for purposes as diverse as a new aircraft and the intricacies of contemporary building. Information which has been gained by individual research must be handed on for use by others. It will be readily conceded that there is no better way than for this information to be given in graphic form.

This makes for rapid component recognition and even solves language difficulties. Easier assembly by semi-skilled operatives is achieved as well as more intelligent understanding of complicated general arrangement drawings by non-technicians. Isometric and planometric views, exploded and cut-away projections are excellent for technical illustrations for sales catalogues, instruction manuals and spare parts lists.

To visualise a complicated project from a multitude of plans, elevations and sections in orthographic projection is no mean task for the non-technician. The designer/draughtsman avoids numerous headaches and explanations because in the end time is saved, if he prepares an accurate three-dimensional illustration to supplement his English or American projection drawings.

Illustration 3 (diagrams 1, 2 and 3) show a spatial construction which could be the basic design for an exhibition stand or kiosk, and summarises in a striking manner the fundamental differences between English Projection and Isometric and Axonometric Planometric Projections. Diagrams 2 and 3 prove conclusively the advantages of supplementing the normal, orthographic projection, working drawings with three-dimensional technical illustrations which clarify form,

7

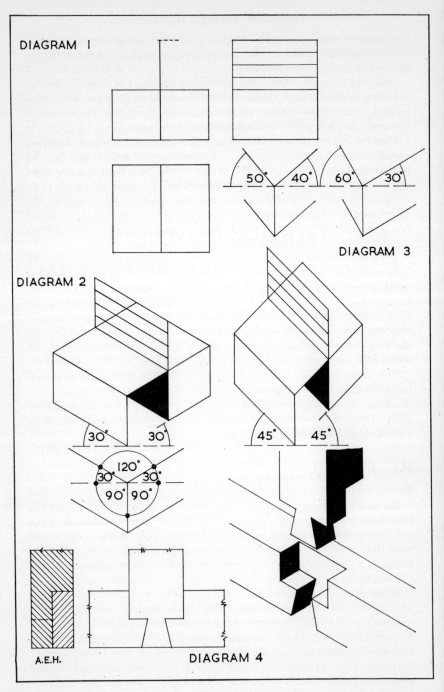

DIAGRAM 1

DIAGRAM 3

DIAGRAM 2

A.E.H.

DIAGRAM 4

3 Isometric and axonometric projections; exploded and cut-away views

construction and design. Diagram 1 in English projection shows that even the professional, let alone the layman, might have great difficulty in reading the designer's intentions.

Diagram 3 represents this solid, having negative and positive volumes, without any ambiguity in Axonometric/Planometric Projection. This system of space projection, unlike Isometric Projection, is not pure geometry but is a convention. Axonometric or Planometric Projection is very popular with contemporary architects and planners, which curiously overcomes the apparent incorrect 'perspective' of isometry. All right angles in the orthographic plan view remain right angles in the axonometric view; therefore the plan views at their respective heights or levels remain true plans and can be rotated at the most suitable angles at the draughtsman's discretion, the more usual being 45°/45°, 50°/40° and 60°/30°. In all cases, of course, vertical lines are drawn to the same scale as the rotated plan.

Diagram 2 shows, on the other hand, the same 'construction' in isometry. This is based on the plan of a cube when its diagonal is vertical therefore all faces of the solid are equally inclined to the horizontal plane, each of the upper three faces being parallel to one of the lower three. The supplementary figure below the diagram shows that the three isometric axes are drawn by making three equal angles; the height of the object will be on the vertical axis and the length and width of it on the other two axes which are always at 30° respectively.

The orthographic view, diagram 1, is almost unintelligible—even to the initiated—but supported by one of the two space projections, diagrams 2 and 3, the draughtsman's intentions are immediately clear. Diagram 4 shows how useful isometry can be in portraying exploded views of construction.

Mechanical Aid

The *Perspector* is a clever mechanical aid for producing isometric views and is in general use in drawing offices of many famous firms in this country and overseas. The manufacturers claim that the use of the machine greatly reduces the time to execute isometric drawings and that they are outstanding for their accuracy and clarity particularly for spare part catalogue illustrations and anything of a similar nature.

The *Perspector* has been evolved as an additional aid for the draughtsman, in fact, his own machine tool for speed and accuracy, and by intelligent operation opens up a very wide field of usefulness. The difficulty of drawing numerous accurate ellipses and elliptical sections is a very real one. The *Perspector* with its dual pantograph, its fixed and moving drawing boards, produces ellipses of true isometric proportions, 0·577:1, as well as curves and straight lines accurate in their geometric proportions without the necessity of elaborate plotting.

The isometric draughtsman will undoubtedly appreciate this unique and completely revolutionary equipment which will enable him to produce an even higher standard of drawing than before with less fatigue, greater precision and higher speed

Illustration 14, by permission of High Precision Equipment Ltd, illustrates some of the possibilities of the *Perspector*. The first section (at the top) is left just as it came from the machine; it can either be prepared for diagrammatic use as has been done in the centre section or finished with an air brush technique for catalogue or publicity purposes. Note that the illustration can be either horizontal, vertical or at any of the axonometric conventional angles. Having set the relative position of fixed and moving drawing boards, the draughtsman has only to follow the form on the plan drawing. The dual pantograph does the work of plotting and translation of orthographic drawings into isometric or 'picture drawings', the mechanism of the *Perspector* being the brain. For example, the draughtsman follows the form of a circle on the plan drawing on the fixed board, and the machine draws the ellipse on the moving board. Composite forms are translated with equal ease. All straight lines normal to the centre line of the machine are drawn by a simple movement of the moving board motivated by a hand wheel.

SECTION 2

Technical Illustrating: A

THREE-POINT PERSPECTIVE PROJECTION

or Vertical Perspective, as it is sometimes called in Aeronautical and Engineering Projects

This is the case for the use of the third vanishing point. Perspective is understood by relatively few artists and draughtsmen with the result that drawings are often dubious and dangerously misleading. Perspective renderings of aeroplanes and motorcars reproduced in the trade journals and in the glossy periodicals are very often vague artists' impressions conveying an exaggerated length or 'lowness'.

Engineers' perspective, on the other hand, has precise definite rules. The technical illustrator, or the designer preparing a presentation drawing, must be very volume and space conscious. He must understand the theory of the picture plane, the ground plane, the eye level/horizon line, centre of vision, focal point, vanishing points including the third vanishing point, the cone of visual rays, the positioning of the spectator, reflections, sciagraphy and the perspective of cast shadows.

Perspective Projection Simplified

The author has dealt exhaustively with all these basic principles of the art of perspective in *Trade Draughtsmanship* (B. T. Batsford Ltd). Therefore it would be mere repetition to recapitulate in the present work, with one exception—the reference to, and a development of, the author's simplified basic method of engineers' perspective.

Three-point perspective or vertical perspective, the most natural of perspective projections, is now a normal drawing office procedure and it is possibly the most important single factor in the work of the technical illustrator producing original drawings. Isometric and planometric projections, in spite of their usefulness for many purposes, are too diagrammatic for the effective interpretation of, for example, an engine layout, an aircraft or a motor vehicle.

Illustration 4, is by permission of the Mavitta Drafting Machines Ltd. The fundamental principles of three-point perspective are best explained by means of a cube, arranged in such a way that the top, or bottom, and two sides are presented to the spectator to the best

11

possible advantage. Now by visualizing an aeroplane placed inside the transparent cube it will follow that its perspective will be the same as the cube. Note that these positions produce three different views of the *Britannia*, dependent upon which axis becomes the vertical one, and

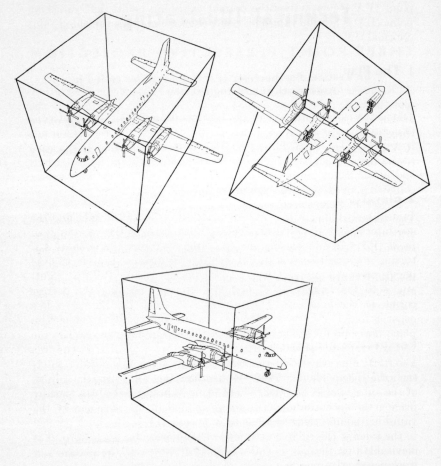

4 Mavitta Drafting Machines Ltd. Demonstration of three-point perspective

whether the perspective of the cube converges to the vertical vanishing points, upwards or downwards respectively.

Illustration 5 demonstrates Three-point Perspective Projection. This presents the logical development of the author's simplified engineers' method as described in *Trade Draughtsmanship*. In three-point perspective the spectator's central visual ray (C.V.R.) and the picture plane (P.P.), on which the perspective is projected must be at *right-angles* to one another, irrespective of the position of the object to be delineated, otherwise distorted perspective occurs. The intention here is to show, as simply as possible, how to plot the vertical vanishing point (V.V.P.) as well as the normal vanishing points, left vanishing point (L.V.P.), right vanishing point (R.V.P.) and 90° vanishing point (Normal C.V.).

1 The Plan

As is shown in the lower half of the left-hand side of the illustration, plot the basic cube at 36° and 54° respectively; this rotation is in the author's experience the most successful for the eventual plotting of the three concurrent scaled axes. Draw the spectator's central visual ray (C.V.R.) exactly opposite the *focal point* (F.P.) which is at the very centre of the cube.

2 Elevations

Immediately above it is plotted the side elevation of the cube and the spectator's central visual ray looking downwards at $28\frac{1}{2}°$ to the *focal point* (F.P.). Avoid placing the spectator over-near the cube as distorting is bound to occur. In this instance the distance is perfect as the perspective will prove. Construct the picture plane (P.P.) at right-angles to the central visual ray (C.V.R.) and touching the nearest corner of the cube; the horizon line (on which the normal V.P.'s occur) is found in the usual manner, i.e. a line constructed on the picture plane horizontally in alignment with the spectator's eye (EYE); the vertical vanishing point downwards is found by projecting downwards a vertical line, parallel to the vertical lines of the cube until it intersects the picture plane; visual rays are taken from the eye to the corners of the cube intersecting the picture plane. Complete the plan view by placing the spectator's eye, from which find in the normal way the vanishing points, right and left (R.V.P. and L.V.P.) by lines parallel to the sides of the cube, on the plan of the horizontal line. [Note: it is inevitable that the side elevation, the plan view and the perspective workings overlap due to a desire to make them large.]

3 Perspective

At the right-hand side of the paper set this up in alignment with the side elevation . . . draw the ground line of the horizontal plane on which is placed the cube; this plane as it is in parallel perspective will vanish to the C.V. (this is the position of a normal C.V. when the C.V.R. is parallel to the ground plane). The perspective positions of all corners

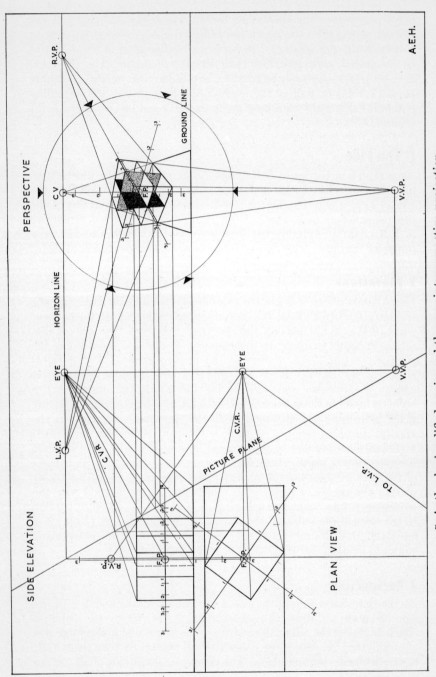

5 Author's simplified engineers' three-point perspective projection

6 Technical illustrator's perspective grid on which a cube has been drawn

Technical illustrator's perspective grid

of the cube are found at the intersections of the visual rays with the picture plane which are transferred to the plan for widths and to the perspective view for heights; from these locations lines are taken to the L.V.P., the R.V.P. and the V.V.P. respectively.

4 The Axes

The cube is now developed egg-crate-wise showing the major planes (represented respectively by white, black and fine dots) mutually at right-angles to one another, the central point of intersection is the *focal point* (F.P.). Three lines passing through this point lie in their respective planes and converge to the L.V.P., the R.V.P. and the V.V.P. respectively which become the three *concurrent axes* on which heights, depths and widths are scaled.

5 Units of Measurement

On plan and in elevation the three axes are subdivided, and the divisions extended to give the bases for the perspective scales *in units of measurement originating from the focal point* (F.P.). Project the three scaled axes as the main lines of the cube were dealt with. The three graduated axes for the heights, depths and widths so obtained are scaled in measuring units which diminish towards the vanishing points, with the L.V.P., the R.V.P. and the V.V.P. and are sufficient for the direct construction of three-point perspective views. Each of the three scaled axes of the perspective view must be correlated with three lines drawn centrally on the orthographic projection of machine part, aeroplane, motorcar, etc., i.e. on the plan view of the project draw two lines, fore and aft directions, at right-angles intersecting centrally, to obtain the focal point; complete by projecting these two lines to the side and end views respectively and by erecting a vertical intersecting the focal point for heights. Diagram A of Illustration 15 by permission of Mavitta Drafting Machines Ltd makes this procedure clear.

The kind of perspective likely to be most useful in engineering may appear involved in a written explanation but, however, it is not difficult when once grasped. To lessen this labour, fortunately, the technical illustrator has devices, such as grids, and even a mechanical aid at his service, but both helps are constructed on the methods described above.

6 The Scaled Grid or 'Perspective Frame'

This very useful device can be made by the illustrator himself provided he understands fully the theory above. Scaled grids are developed from the 'egg-crate' construction shown in perspective in Illustration 5. The use of distant vanishing points, which require large drawing

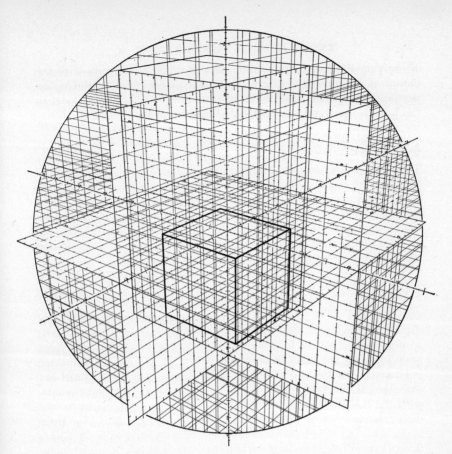

7 A demonstration perspective grid

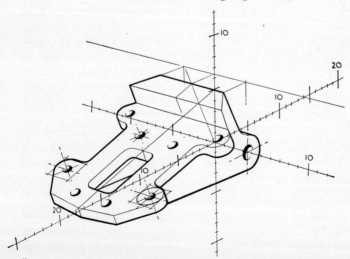

8 Hawker Aircraft Ltd. A component drawn on the grid

boards, presents great difficulties when perspectives of engines, motor-cars and aeroplanes are wanted. Consequently the artist enlarges, perhaps by photography, the small scale grid, complete with the three perspective axes and scales. This is traced and blue prints for future use produced.

Illustrations 6 and 7 demonstrate the possibilities of the grid. An illustrator in the Technical Publications Department can select from a number of grids the most suitable for any particular purpose, which obviates the drawing up of special grids. Illustrations 6 and 7 present three grids on two of which a cube has been drawn; in each case one unit on the grid represents a measurement to the desired scale. The draughtsman selects a grid or part of a grid that will give the best view of the object to be drawn, which might range from a simple component (illustrations 8 and 10) to a complete aeroplane (illustration 4, three views). Note that a cube drawn on different parts of the grid will be of different shape and also that the grid can be upside down for underneath views or on its side to give a different set of angles. The divisions on the main lines of the grid can represent any suitable size which of course must be the same for each of the three lines.

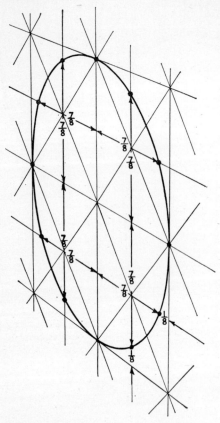

9 Enlarged diagram to show the $\frac{7}{8}$ principle of constructing an ellipse

The appropriate grid for the job to be undertaken is affixed to the drawing board with drafting tape and a sheet of thin but firm tracing paper, through which the grid and its scales are clearly seen, is also affixed to the surface with drafting tape. It is customary in some offices to show the main constructional lines in red and/or blue as an aid to identification and quick reference because some perspective projects are of great complexity. Finally, the

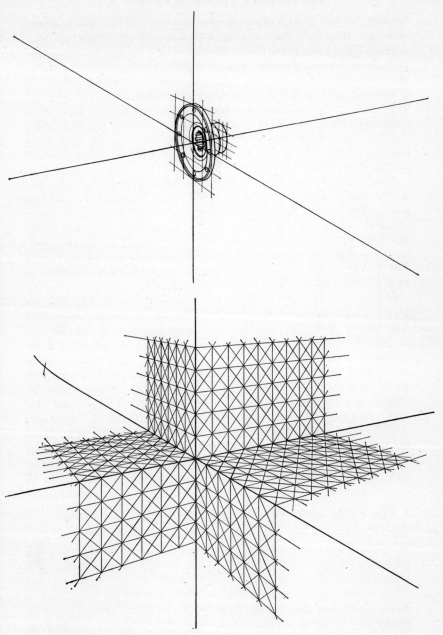

10 Perspective grid devised by A.E.C. Limited with a component drawn on the grid

drawing, on the tracing paper, is transferred to a quality line board for 'inking-in' and rendered either in black and white or colour.

Illustration 7 is a particularly interesting and intriguing perspective grid. Students who are using the grid sytem for the first time will find that this particular grid will make it easier for them to grasp its possibilities and to understand the various planes.

Illustration 8 is a drawing, specially made for this work, of a component made on this grid and is reproduced by courtesy of Hawker Aircraft Ltd, Kingston-on-Thames. The constructional lines have purposely been left. *Note:* The three scaled axes with the units of measurement originating from the focal point.

Illustration 10 is by courtesy of A.E.C. Limited. This grid serves exactly the same purpose as the three just studied. Although perspective is virtually an exact science, artists interpret it in a very personal way, as an aid, as these four grids conclusively prove. Study the simple component which has been drawn on the perspective grid, and note how the ellipses have been constructed and finally drawn. The enlarged illustration 9 makes clear the 7/8 principle of constructing or plotting ellipses by professional technical artists.

Illustrations 11 and 12 are Crown copyright, reproduced with the permission of the Controller of H.M. Stationery Office. They represent respectively the front fuselage and rear fuselage of the *Hawker P1101—Two-seater Hunter*. They were produced (on the three point perspective grid in the Technical Publications Department) by the technical illustrators of Hawker Aircraft Ltd. These perfect black and white illustrations prove beyond argument that the most complicated illustrations are possible by using one of the many variants of the grid made personally by the illustrator (without recourse to a specially made drawing board cut along arcs struck from the three V.P.s) provided the draughtsmen, as in these cases, are extremely able. The illustrations were reproduced and printed by the 'Multilith' photographic litho method in the originals.

7 The Three-point Perspective Board

The artist himself can also make a perspective board cut along arcs struck from the three vanishing points for very personal work. But for a standardised system, the use of the *Mavitta 3 D Drawing Board* has eliminated many difficulties usually encountered. It is based on the fundamental principles of perspective which the author has explained and undoubtedly makes for speed in the constructional stages of a perspective drawing. The drawing board, cut along arcs struck from the vanishing points, consists of a flat white surface on which are imprinted the three scaled axes. On the underside of the board are three curved slots, that contain and guide the heads of the transparent

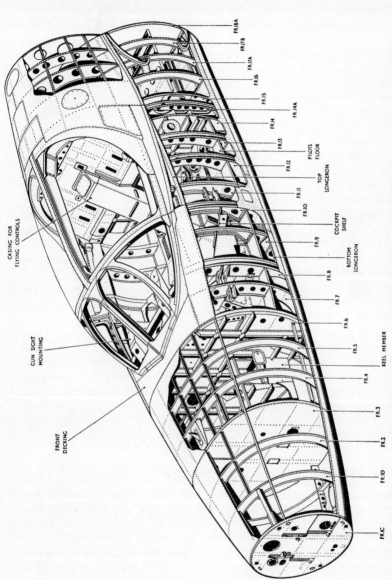

CASING FOR
FLYING CONTROLS

GUN SIGHT
MOUNTING

FRONT
DECKING

FR.I8A
FR.I7B
FR.I7A
FR.I6
FR.I5
FR.I4A
FR.I4
FR.I3
FR.I2
PILOTS
FLOOR
FR.II
TOP
LONGERON
FR.IO
COCKPIT
SHELF
FR.9
BOTTOM
LONGERON
FR.8
FR.7
FR.6
FR.5
KEEL MEMBER
FR.4
FR.3
FR.2
FR.ID
FR.C

11 H.M. Stationery Office. Front fuselage. Hawker P 1101 two-seater Hunter (drawn on grid)

Crown copyright

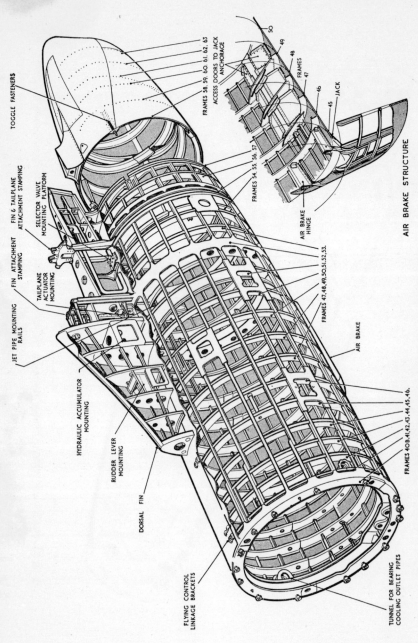

TOGGLE FASTENERS

FIN & TAILPLANE
ATTACHMENT STAMPING

SELECTOR VALVE
MOUNTING PLATFORM

FIN ATTACHMENT
STAMPING

TAILPLANE
ACTUATOR
MOUNTING

JET PIPE MOUNTING
RAILS

HYDRAULIC ACCUMULATOR
MOUNTING

RUDDER LEVER
MOUNTING

DORSAL FIN

FLYING CONTROL
LINKAGE BRACKETS

TUNNEL FOR BEARING
COOLING OUTLET PIPES

FRAMES 58. 59. 60. 61. 62. 63

ACCESS DOORS TO JACK
ANCHORAGE

50

49

48

FRAMES
47

46

45

JACK

FRAMES 54. 55. 56. 57

AIR BRAKE
HINGE

AIR BRAKE STRUCTURE

FRAMES 47, 48, 49, 50, 51, 52, 53.

AIR BRAKE

FRAMES 40B. 41, 42, 43, 44, 45, 46.

Crown copyright

12 H.M. Stationery Office. Rear fuselage. Hawker P 1101 two-seater Hunter drawn on grid

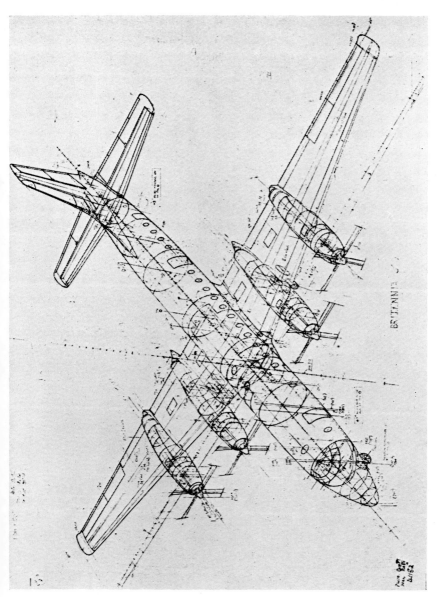

13 Bristol Aircraft Ltd.   Constructional drawing of the *Britannia 300*

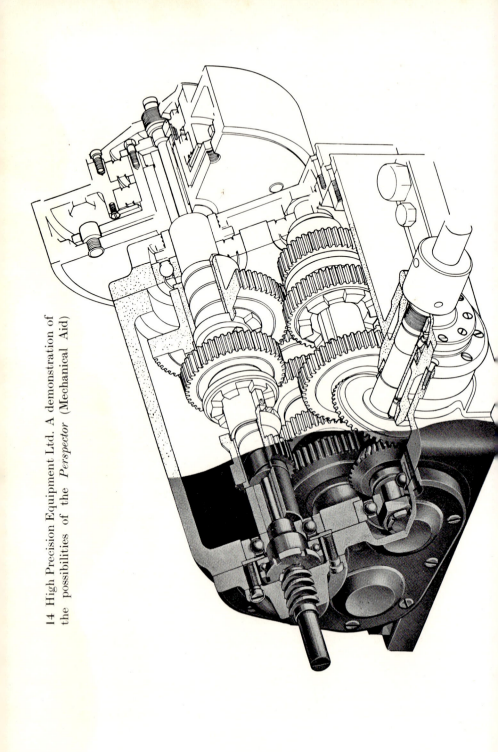

14 High Precision Equipment Ltd. A demonstration of the possibilities of the *Perspector* (Mechanical Aid)

lineads, each of which has a drawing edge, thus providing the means of drawing lines which will converge towards their correct vanishing points. The board may be rotated on its base in order to present the illustrator with any of the six positions shown in the author's perspective method in illustration 5.

The perspective board is just another drawing instrument and should be treated as such. It does not draw for the illustrator, it provides an aid to producing an accurate perspective construction of any object.

The illustrator in using either his own grid, or the 3 D perspective board, should construct that amount of framework which will enable him to develop a technique in which his own natural gifts are used to the full.

Illustration 13 by kind permission of Bristol Aircraft Ltd. The technical illustrators in the drawing offices of this organisation make full use of the *Mavitta 3 D Drawing Board* in the preparation of aircraft drawings. This setting out of a *Britannia 300* is particularly instructive as all the constructional lines can clearly be seen. Methods for constructing ellipses are propounded in the following section. Study Illustration 16, also compare the constructive drawing of the *Britannia* with the finalised illustrations shown in Illustrations 75 and 76.

Finally, perspective drawings are widely used in industry today as an invaluable aid in all stages from the original 'doodle', for the actual design stage, through production to the utilisation of the finished product. Their use as an instant aid to recognition of components in spare parts lists, catalogues, brochures, instruction books and technical manuals is universal. Perspectives call for special skill on the part of the draughtsman who must have a very clear understanding of what the 'solid' view will look like and, in addition, a knowledge of illustrating techniques and craftsmanship.

Technical Illustrating: B

TECHNICAL DESCRIPTIVE DRAUGHTSMANSHIP

1 Plotting a Project in Three-point Perspective

Perspective views of industrial productions are developed by plotting points, their positions being found by scaled off measurements with engineers' scales. It is of paramount importance that *all measurements originate from the focal point* and also along the height, depth and width axes. In the previous section it was stated that the divisions on the main lines of the grid, or on the 3 D drawing board, can represent any

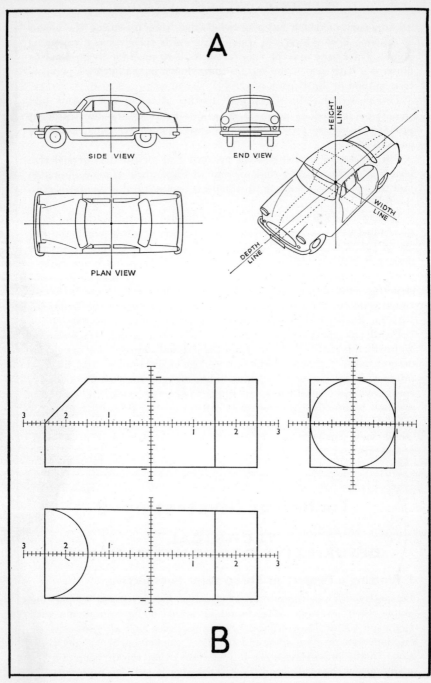

A

SIDE VIEW

END VIEW

PLAN VIEW

HEIGHT LINE

WIDTH LINE

DEPTH LINE

B

15 Mavitta Drafting Machines Ltd. Plotting a project in three-point perspective

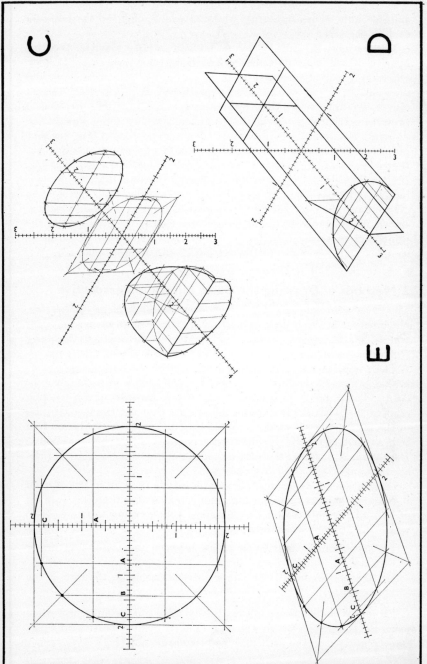

C   D   E

16 Mavitta Drafting Machines Ltd. Methods of drawing the basic ellipse in perspective

suitable unit of measurement, which of course must be the same for each of the three axes.

Illustrations 15 and 16 by permission of the Mavitta Drafting Machines Ltd, show five illustrations from their instruction booklet. Diagram A (already referred to, p. 26 (5. Units of Measurements)) and diagrams B, C and D, the latter depicting views of a simple abstract object, carefully chosen in order to illustrate the procedure involved in projecting the fundamental shapes encountered in three-dimensional drawing. Diagram A, of a motorcar in orthographic and 3 D perspective projection demonstrates the application of the procedure already mentioned (p. 14 (5)), in relation to *depth* line, *width* line and *height* line. If such lines do not exist on the orthographic views, draw them, as is indicated in the diagram, as centrally as possible, their intersection determining the *focal point*. An analysis of the recommended method shown in diagrams B, C and D indicates clearly the approach to the projection of these basic forms and of their application to forms as complex as those shown in Illustration 13 of a Bristol *Britannia*.

2 Methods of Drawing the Basic Ellipse in Perspective

The circle is the continually recurring geometrical theme in engineering. Machinery contains a large proportion of cylindrical forms, such as gear wheels, shafts, gauges, pistons. Many industrial products are basically cylindrical as numerous illustrations in this work prove.

The perspective of a circle is a perfect ellipse and the cardinal rule is that a minor axis must be always at right angles to its major axis. (Note: The principle properties of the ellipse, methods of constructing ellipses, (a) given the major and minor axes (but not the foci), (b) use of the ancillary circle, and (c) by the trammel method, can be referred to in a standard practical geometry and engineering graphics text book.) Having once mastered the drawing of the ellipse the draughtsman has another important asset at his service.

Illustration 16, diagram E, as mentioned above, is from the *Mavitta* instruction booklet. The accompanying text states that the drawing of ellipses presents a difficulty for most people owing to two factors, which the author can confirm:

(i) The infinite variation in ratios between the major and minor axes.

(ii) The positioning of the ellipse in relationship to the rest of the drawing.

These two problems are automatically solved in a simple way when using the perspective board which produces scaled perspective drawings directly related to the orthographic originals.

Consider the circle from which the ellipse is desired. This circle can

28

be enclosed in a square whose sides are equal to the diameter of the circle, it follows that if the perspective of the square is drawn, then the ellipse must fit in that shape. Further, if a number of points are established on the circle, they, in turn, may be plotted within the perspective of the square, thus providing points through which the perspective of the circle will pass.

Conveniently printed on the board's surface is a simple graph from which the co-ordinates of three points lying in a quadrant of a circle may be read off for any given radius. Should the illustrator wish to draw a large ellipse very accurately, there need be no limit to the number of points he may plot from the original circle.

It is strongly recommended that the illustrator develops the ability to draw with precision, in freehand, the curves passing through plotted points such as those which occur in ellipses, etc. The power of draughtsmanship thus gained will prove invaluable in speedily completing first rate drawings within the accurate framework of perspective. It will be appreciated by readers that the author's 'egg-crate' three-point perspective grid with its central focal point (Illustration 5) and the three three-point perspective grids as devised and used by the illustrating artists in the aircraft industry (Illustrations 6 and 7); and the very individual solution to the grid by the illustrators in the drawing office of A.E.C. Limited (Illustration 10), lend themselves perfectly to the procedural advice given above in reference to the use of the *Mavitta 3 D Drawing Board*. This drawing board has one great advantage over these illustrator-devised perspective grids, although all are based on the same fundamentals of focal point and scaled axes, and that is increased versatility and speed in the constructional stages of a setting out.

To sum up, a complete mastery of three-point perspective will in practice prove to be practical, relatively simple and unfailingly accurate, for the delineation of objects common to industry and commerce. Once the fundamental principles are fully understood by the illustrator he is able to prepare perspective drawings, by any one of the above methods, of projects as involved as an aircraft or an atomic reactor.

Technical Illustrating: C

TECHNICAL DESCRIPTIVE ILLUSTRATION

The Interpretation of Engineering Drawings

The engineering draughtsman who is producing machine drawings in orthographic projection works to established rules and formulae, in an idiom which is a technical language, intelligible to other technicians, but not as a rule to those who are not trained engineers. Photography communicates intelligence that they can comprehend, but is, by its very nature, superficial in so far as details of function and construction are concerned. Consequently neither will give all the answers sought by the uninitiated.

Conversely, the *explanatory drawing* in all its possible forms, interprets intelligently the facts of the case for all to read and understand. The technical illustrators, or artists, who produce these rendered or line drawings have certain essential qualifications and have acquired the fundamental skills and must have had a minimum technical training. In brief, they must combine artistic ability, mechanical understanding and be expert in precision drawing.

Every branch of human endeavour, whether it be engineering, industry generally or science, adopts its own special method of graphic explanation as the most appropriate form of intelligence, which could be any one of the three-dimensional techniques available to the technical illustrator.

Briefly there are five types of explanatory descriptive illustrations to interpret graphically pure engineering drawings:

(1) Three-dimensional perspective views from orthographic projections.
(2) Exploded views on horizontal centre lines throughout the diameters of all co-axially-aligned components.
(3) Cut-away drawings and phantom sectionised or ghosted views.
(4) Diagrammatic representations (not to be confused with schematic illustrations or outline dimension drawings).
(5) Free-perspective draughtsmanship based on judgment.

These five methods of illustrating, i.e. the pictorial means of communicating design and mechanical intelligence to others, demand exacting qualities of draughtsmanship, in fact a cold machine-tooled precision of hand and eye for such literature as illustrated parts catalogues and maintenance manuals.

The choice of one of these types of explanatory descriptive illustration will depend upon the type of intelligence it is intended to impart, for instance, exploded views should be used to support assembly and dismantling instructions, parts lists, etc. (Illustration 22) and, on the other hand, free perspective should be used to present the appearance of a projection in readily understandable form (Illustrations 17, 18). Their value lies in the fact that, although they are highly technical subject matter, they do not call for exceptional 'know-how' for their comprehension, i.e. they are intended to give others that kind of information which helps them to understand specific features of design, construction, to portray controls, operating principles and generally to support

30

17 and 18 British Motor Corporation Ltd. *Austin Seven 850* (above) looking through open door; (below) rear end with open locker

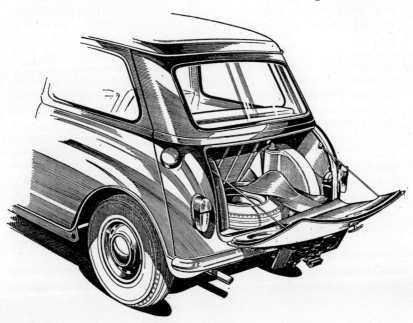

descriptive text. The information could not readily be imparted by any other means. All conform to recognised practices in the respective industries.

Technical descriptive illustration calls for unusual skill from the artist particularly in the more complex drawings where execution and clarity of presentation must be outstanding. Many of the excellent illustrations in this work prove they are often works of art in their own right.

Many of the illustrations used in the foregoing sections to exemplify various methods and principles make use of some of the pictorial means we are about to consider in detail for their own sakes.

1 Perspective Drawings from 'Blue Prints'

The technical illustrator's lifelike portrayal in perspective of a new project which is often just at the 'blue print' stage. This is a very acceptable type of illustration relatively easy for all to understand. The artist is the link between the engineering draughtsman and the 'man-in-the-street' presenting facts in a readily understandable form. The essential high standard of finish is only possible if the illustrator exercises skill and patience.

Illustration 19 is reproduced by courtesy of Vauxhall Motors Ltd. This beautifully finished half-tone perspective drawing from 'blue prints' skilfully shows the design both externally and internally (by means of the cut-away sectional technique) of the front drive axle—*Bedford R.4.×4* truck. This also has been 'washed-up'. Originally reproduced by letterpress—H/T block, 133 screen copper cut-out.

Illustration 20 is also by courtesy of Vauxhall Motors Ltd. It is interesting to note that this example was drawn from actual parts, 'washed-up' (technical terminology for rendered) for half-tone reproduction. This was a letterpress H/T block, 133 screen copper cut-out (and also was produced by offset litho). This simple straightforward drawing in perspective of the Bedford diesel engine connecting rod and piston is taken from a brochure for Bedford Trucks. This type of rendered component leaves nothing to be desired and is worthy of emulation.

Illustrations 17 and 18 are reproduced by permission of the British Motor Corporation Ltd. They show two views in penmanship of the new *Austin Seven 850* from the B.M.C.'s publication *Consolidated Technical Data for the Austin Seven 850* and an identical book was produced for the *Morris Mini-Minor*. The view looking through the open door is very informative and instructive for the student. Note particularly the various line techniques employed by the illustrator to suggest the materials used. The rear end with the open locker lid employs

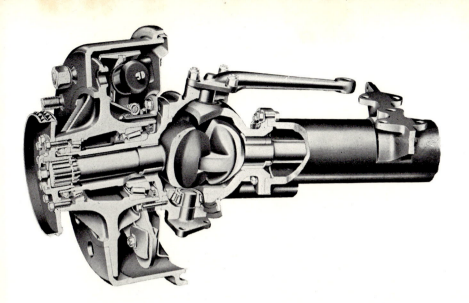

19 Vauxhall Motors Ltd. Front-
drive axle of *Bedford R. 4 × 4* truck.
Cut-away and 'washed-up'

20 Vauxhall Motors Ltd. *Bedford*
diesel engine connecting rod and
piston 'washed-up'

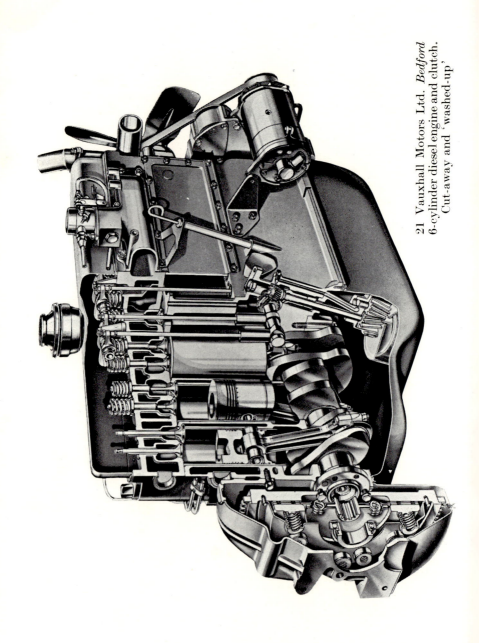

21 Vauxhall Motors Ltd. *Bedford* 6-cylinder diesel engine and clutch. Cut-away and 'washed-up'

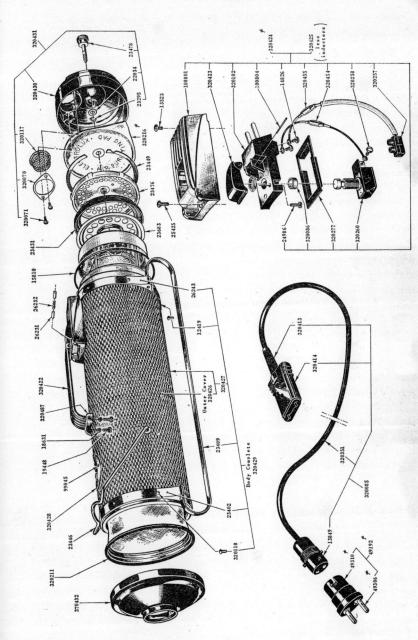

22 Electrolux Ltd. Electrolux Suction cleaner, *Model 60*, exploded

typical line techniques brilliantly. Both detail drawings do credit to Alec Issigonis' conception.

2 Exploded Views from Data

An exploded view of an object is given when the components are taken apart, but placed co-axially so that compression along their respective arcs would result in re-assembly. Many examples will be found among the illustrations in this volume.

Illustrations 22, 23, 24 and 25 are by courtesy of Electrolux Ltd. All are from their spare parts lists and prove that the line drawing is the most acceptable type for such purposes. In addition, they demonstrate the type of illustration which is universally used by those industries manufacturing consumer goods such as these: vacuum cleaners, floor polishers, refrigerators and scores of other products. This type of illustration should be used throughout the parts lists, should be used to support assembly and dismantling instructions and wherever detail arrangement is required. Exploded perspective draughtsmanship is particularly informative as every component can be shown in due relationship, from a screw to a cover plus its recognition annotation number. All these illustrations demonstrate that the illustrator, with only black and white at his disposal, is able to produce drawings in readily understandable form, for instance, the floor polisher—a rare example of *vertical* explosion—clearly shows the various finishes and materials by fine dots, lines, solid black and white. This series of illustrations produced by artists for a universally-known organisation is a most valuable case-history of its methods in the field of illustration.

Illustration 26 is reproduced by courtesy of Rolls-Royce Ltd. This is the rear bearing housing of the Rolls-Royce *Dart* propeller turbine. This is also an unusual exploded arrangement but is typical of Rolls-Royce's practice of exploding on a *curved* axis which allows the illustrator to show all the components in a small area, in simple line drawing with a minimum of shading.

3 Cut-Away Drawings and Phantom Views

Cut-away drawings are graphic reproductions of the sectionised object, revealing parts of the exterior surface and slicing into the object to show the arrangement and workings of the interior at a prearranged point. Phantom views are invaluable for detailing an installation and are used extensively in the descriptive matter to portray systems, controls, power plants, internal installations, etc. Sectioned perspective drawings expose salient features of internal design and reveal methods of operation.

Illustration 21 is reproduced by permission of Vauxhall Motors Ltd. This is a very beautifully drawn and rendered cut-away sectioned

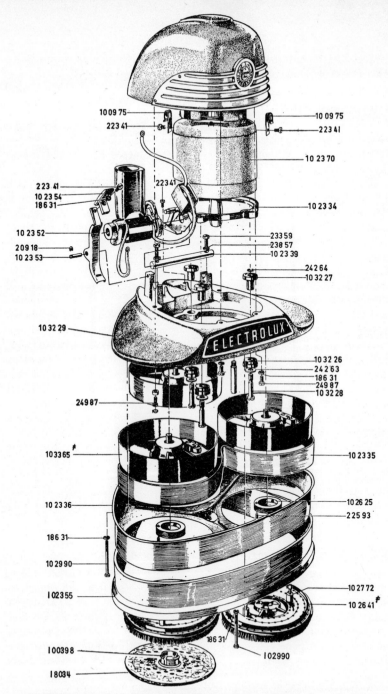

10 09 75
223 41
10 09 75
223 41
10 23 70
2 23 41
10 23 54
186 31
223 41
10 23 34
10 23 52
233 59
238 57
10 23 39
2 09 18
10 23 53
242 64
10 32 27
10 32 29
ELECTROLUX
10 32 26
242 63
186 31
249 87
10 32 28
249 87
10 33 65
10 23 35
10 23 36
10 26 25
2 25 93
186 31
10 29 90
10 27 72
1 023 55
10 26 41
100398
186 31
1 029 90
180 34

23 Electrolux Ltd. Electrolux floor polisher. Vertical explosion

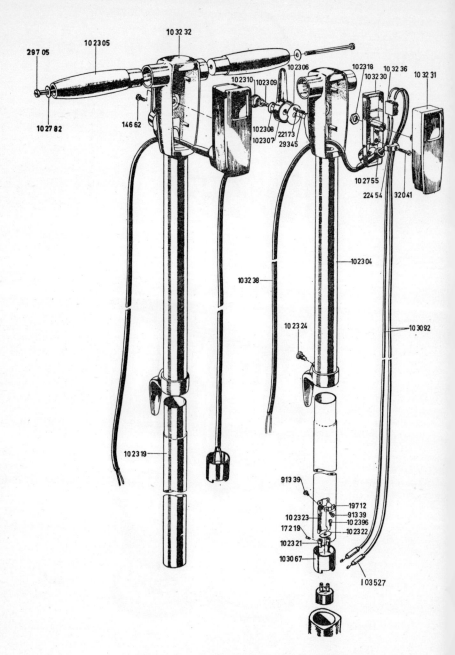

24 Electrolux Ltd. Electrolux floor polisher

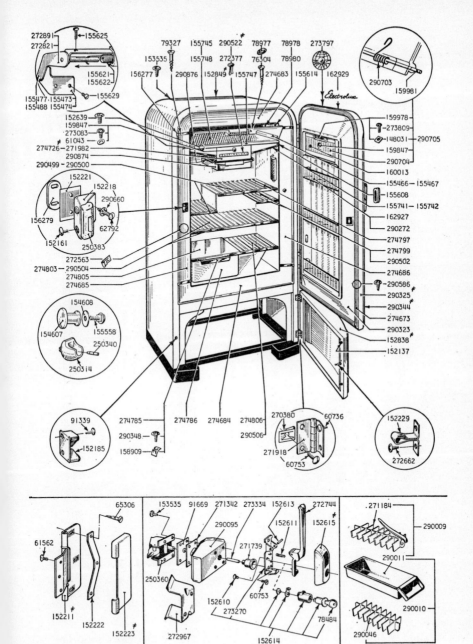

Denotes alternative feature

25 Electrolux Ltd. Electrolux refrigerator. Cabinet parts, *Model L50, b*

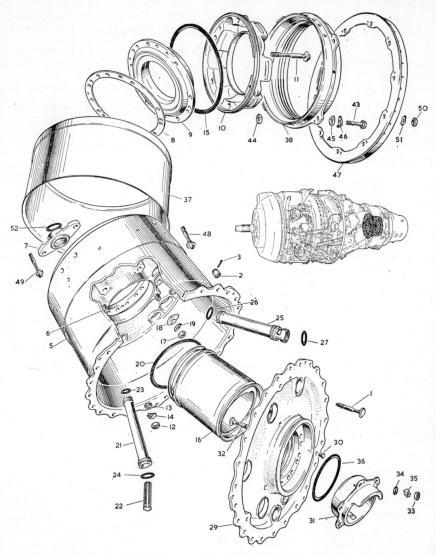

26   Rolls-Royce Ltd. Rear bearing housing of the *Dart* propeller
turbine

perspective drawing from blue prints and 'washed-up' for half-tone reproduction, of the Bedford 6-cylinder diesel engine and clutch. This illustration exposes salient features of internal design which is achieved in a remarkably precise way and was prepared for a booklet entitled *Bedford's Own Diesels* which is an explanation of technical features. Originally reproduced by letterpress—H/T block, 133 screen copper cut-out. Also produced by offset litho.

Illustration 28 is by courtesy of the Standard-Triumph Group, Coventry, England. This very accomplished cut-away illustration represents a sectioned *Vanguard* gearbox. A half-tone, or wash drawing, as it is sometimes called, may be derived from a photograph or line drawing or a combination of both. The combination was employed in this example. A study of the original work 30″ in length emphasises that the process of producing illustrations of this character calls for a high degree of skill on the part of the illustrator.

Blocks

It is well to understand processes of reproduction. Blocks made from the artwork of the Standard-Triumph Group fall into one of four categories:

   (i) Fine line.
  (ii) Deep etchings.
 (iii) Half-tone for which they call for 120 screen on copper.
 (iv) Combination of (ii) and (iii).

The latter type of artwork is avoided wherever possible as the cost of blocks of this nature is high.

Illustration 27 is reproduced by courtesy of Rolls-Royce Ltd. This interesting illustration demonstrates the line technique to reveal method of operation. It is an air compressor—a component of the Rolls-Royce diesel engine. The parallel line and concentric line shading contrasted with the fine dot shading to differentiate finishes and materials is worthy of emulation. The annotation with arrowheads on lead lines leaves nothing to be desired.

Illustration 29 is by courtesy of Vauxhall Motors Ltd. It is an extraordinarily informative drawing proving conclusively the important part the technical artist plays in industry. It is a cut-away perspective drawing, prepared from blue prints and 'washed-up' for half-tone reproduction, of the body-shell of the Vauxhall *PA Velox* and *Cresta*, revealing every form and section for the body-pressers. The illustration is a perfect example of 'washed-up' technique with line emphasis where necessary. Method of reproduction in the original was letterpress—H/T block, 133 screen copper cut-out. This was also used with

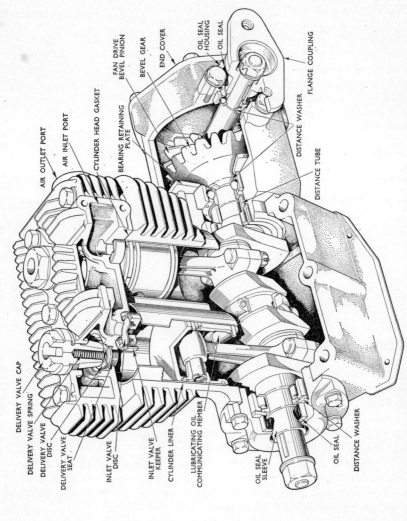

DELIVERY VALVE CAP

DELIVERY VALVE SPRING

DELIVERY VALVE DISC

DELIVERY VALVE SEAT

INLET VALVE DISC

INLET VALVE KEEPER

CYLINDER LINER

LUBRICATING OIL COMMUNICATING MEMBER

OIL SEAL SLEEVE

OIL SEAL

DISTANCE WASHER

AIR OUTLET PORT

AIR INLET PORT

CYLINDER HEAD GASKET

FAN DRIVE BEVEL PINION

BEVEL GEAR

END COVER

BEARING RETAINING PLATE

OIL SEAL HOUSING

OIL SEAL

DISTANCE WASHER

FLANGE COUPLING

DISTANCE TUBE

27 Rolls-Royce Ltd. Air compressor; component of diesel engine in line technique

42

28 Standard Triumph Group. *Vanguard* gearbox cut-away wash drawing

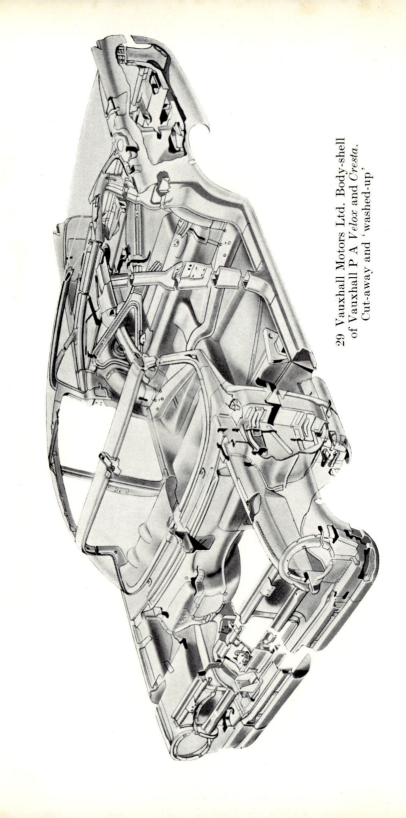

29 Vauxhall Motors Ltd. Body-shell of Vauxhall P A *Velox* and *Cresta*. Cut-away and 'washed-up'

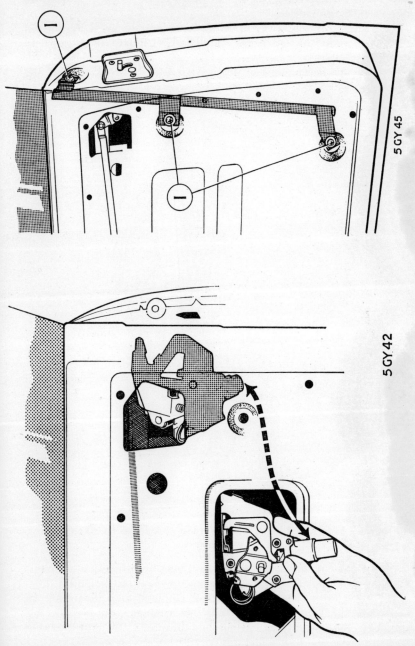

5 GY 45

5 GY 42

30 Diagrams 5 GY 45 and 5 GY 42 show phantom technique

45

tint plate for a second colour for still greater clarity. It was also produced by litho offset.

To digress—this cut-away drawing shows how the quest for lowness plus extra passenger space has stimulated an important advance in motorcar design. It is represented here as a one-piece structure with every inch and every ounce of steel contributing to the strength of the whole.

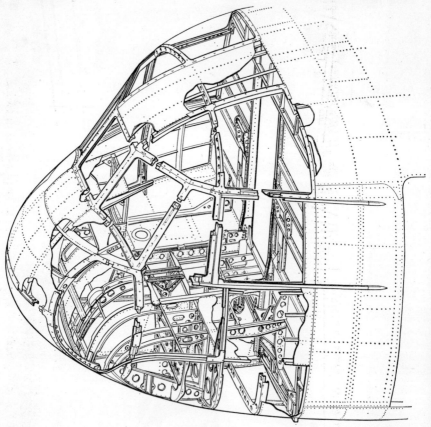

31 Fairey Aviation Ltd. *Rotodyne* pilot's cockpit in line drawing cut-away

Illustrations 31 and 32 are reproduced here by permission of Fairey Aviation Ltd. Illustration 31 is the pilot's cockpit of the Fairey *Rotodyne*, the world's first vertical take-off air liner, and illustration 32 represents the wing structure. Both are examples of line drawing cut-away. Because of low cost the line drawing is the most desirable type of illustration for general use.

Illustration 30 shows two examples of the phantom or ghosted techniques, by courtesy of the Standard-Triumph Group, Coventry. Both are from the *Triumph Herald Workshop Manual* (*Group five*) of the saloon and coupé. Diagram 5 GY 45 illustrates the method to remove the door lock—it shows location of glass run channel securing screws. Conversely diagram 5 GY 42 deals with its re-fitting and shows the fitting lock assembly to door.

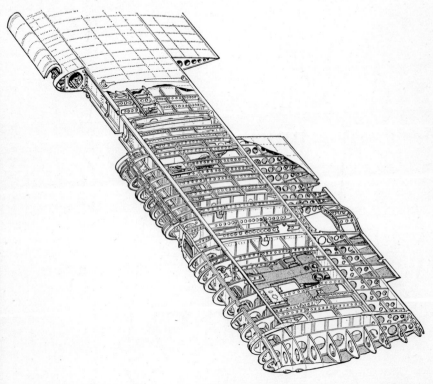

32 Fairey Aviation Ltd. *Rotodyne* wing structure in line drawing cut-away

4 Diagrammatic Representations and Schematics

Diagrammatic representations, either in line or in tone, show in the simplest terms the method of operation, etc. Schematics, always in line, are valuable in detailing principles of a particular system.

Illustration 33 is reproduced by courtesy of Rolls-Royce Ltd. This is an original and clever diagram in cut-away line perspective. The three-dimensional inlet and outlet straight arrows contrasting with the

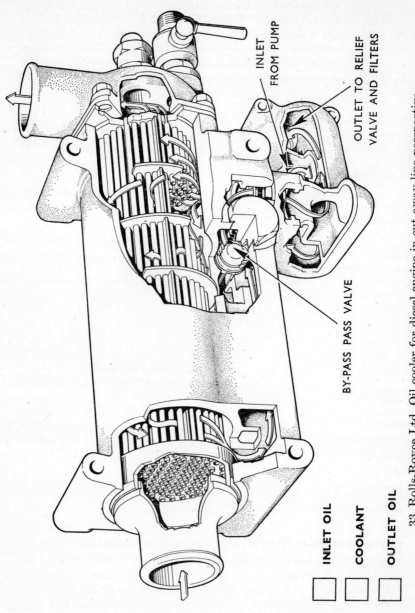

INLET FROM PUMP

OUTLET TO RELIEF VALVE AND FILTERS

BY-PASS PASS VALVE

INLET OIL

COOLANT

OUTLET OIL

33 Rolls-Royce Ltd. Oil cooler for diesel engine in cut-away line perspective

48

curved arrows makes this drawing of an oil cooler for a Rolls-Royce diesel engine self-explanatory.

Illustration 35 is by courtesy of the Standard-Triumph Group. This half-tone sectioned diagram, or wash drawing, as it is sometimes called, of an automatic transmission, was in the first place drawn in black and line, then photographed and the print worked up with the airbrush. This is a very good example also of *round the clock numbering* which will be discussed in detail on page 87.

Illustration 36 is by permission of Vauxhall Motors Ltd and is frankly a sectional drawing from blue prints, 'washed-up' for half-tone reproduction, used with or without typeset overlay. This lubrication system diagram of 300 cu. in. 6-cylinder *Bedford* petrol engine (full pressure, full flow filter system, gear type pump with helical teeth), leaves nothing to be desired—its clarity is emphasised by the dark shading behind the more conventional diagrammatic arrows. Originally made for letterpress—H/T block, 133 or 120 screen, copper cut-out or combined line and tone, was also produced by offset litho.

Illustration 34 is reproduced by courtesy of the Ford Motor Company Ltd, Dagenham, and shows oil flow diagrams for power steering. They are sectional drawings prepared from blue prints of components or assemblies, shaded or stippled to indicate oil flow, with type-set captions. Low pressure fluid is indicated by fine dots and high pressure fluid by solid black. For export market annotations on information illustrations must be in the appropriate foreign language as in this instance. It is not necessary to point out the obvious disadvantages of stencilled or type-set annotations on the art-work itself where the publication is subject to translation. It is good practice to use type-set overlays. Block was fine line zinc or magnesium in the original.

Illustration 38 is by courtesy of Marconi's Wireless Telegraph Company Ltd. This is a plate from the Manual of H.F. Communication Equipment Type AD 307—General Description—and is part of a Block *Schematic Arrangement* illustrating the theory of operation of a multi-channel H.F. communications equipment incorporating automatic tuning facility.

5 Free Draughtsmanship

This is the free use of perspective based on judgment rather than on projection, resulting in illustrative perspective drawings presenting the appearance of the project in readily understandable form ranging from 'doodles' to developed sketches.

Illustration 37, by courtesy of British Olivetti Ltd, presents Olivetti's *Lexicon 80* from 'doodle' stage to its realisation. The body was evolved by Marcello Nizzola who has developed a series of variations and details —such as the line-space lever—which are accounted among the

49

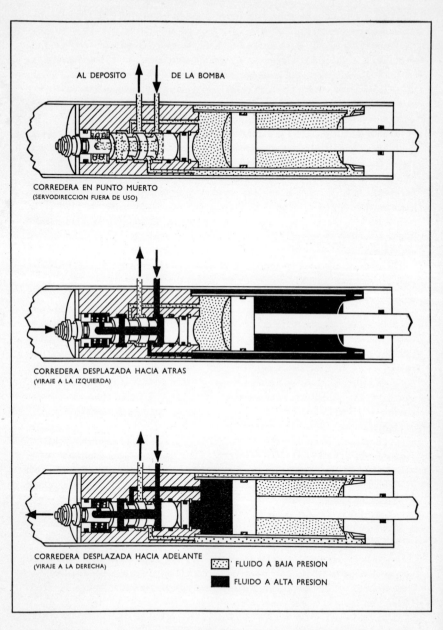

AL DEPOSITO   DE LA BOMBA

CORREDERA EN PUNTO MUERTO
(SERVODIRECCION FUERA DE USO)

CORREDERA DESPLAZADA HACIA ATRAS
(VIRAJE A LA IZQUIERDA)

CORREDERA DESPLAZADA HACIA ADELANTE
(VIRAJE A LA DERECHA)

FLUIDO A BAJA PRESION

FLUIDO A ALTA PRESION

34 Ford Motor Company Ltd. Oil floor. Sectional diagrams for power steering

50

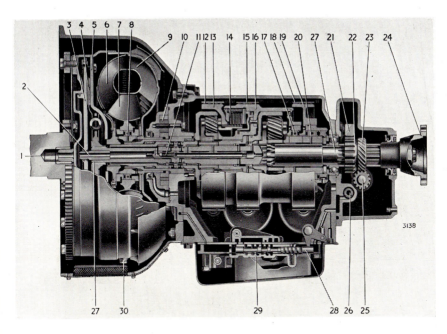

35 Standard Triumph Group. Automatic transmission.
Sectioned wash diagram

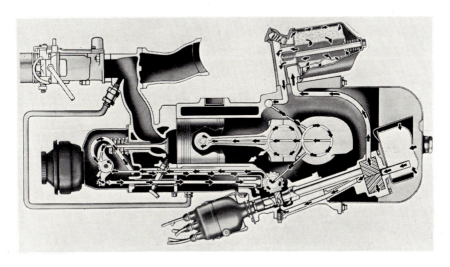

36 Vauxhall Motors Ltd. 300 cu. in. 6-cylinder *Bedford* petrol engine.
Drawing sectional 'washed-up'

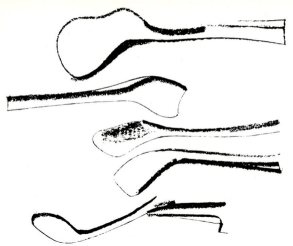

37 British Olivetti Ltd.
Lexicon 80 from doodle
stage to its realization

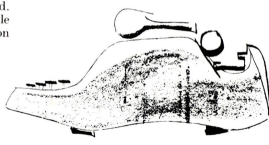

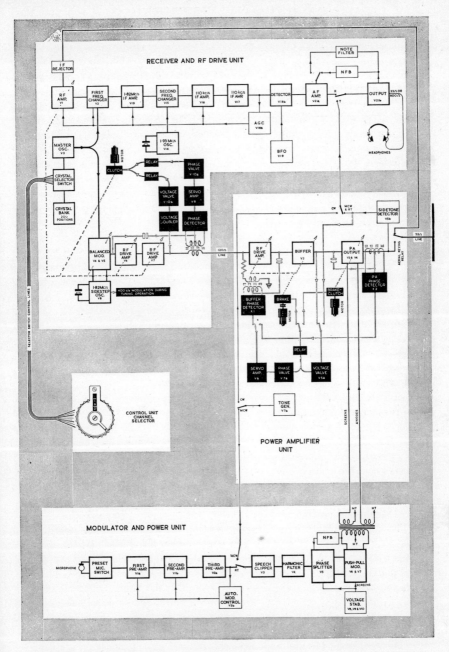

38 Marconi's Wireless Telegraph Company Ltd. Part of Block Schematic
diagram

achievements of Italian contemporary industrial design. Between the conception of the need for a new model and its realisation as a tangible fact, there are many stages from 'doodle' to preliminary working drawings and finally blue prints, which give precise shape to the components, and to the whole, as evolved in the mind of the designer.

Illustration 39, also by courtesy of British Olivetti Ltd, shows the Olivetti *Studio 44* from sketch to model. The elegance, refinement and superb finish have raised our aesthetic senses and provided British designers with new standards against which to measure their own abilities. It is instructive, and an eye-opener, that in the production of photographs of their machines, only ordinary straight photographic processes have been used, and the airbrush was not employed. In the author's view this is the correct approach to creative commercial and technical photography, provided the product has impeccable finish.

Illustrations 40, 42 and 44 are reproduced by courtesy of the Ford Motor Company Ltd. The technique employed in these examples differs from the preceding ones by the Standard-Triumph Group and also they are drawn on a much smaller scale.

Illustration 44. Actual size of drawing measures $13\frac{1}{2}'' \times 10''$. The draughtsman has used white crayon on a french black pastel paper. With the utmost economy of means he has achieved with precision a first-rate impressionistic 'esquisse' showing shape and style—not necessarily correct in every proportion and detail, for the artist is still in command—the engineer has yet to take over.

Illustrations 40 and 42 were drawn on a hot-pressed drawing paper in crayon and wash and were taken beyond the 'doodle' stage although they are still small scale drawings. Illustration 42 shows two able 'esquisses' for a new conception for the *Consul* model and Illustration 40 presents for discussion a proposed new design for the *Zodiac* model.

All the above car body lay-outs present facts in a readily understandable form. This aspect of technical art can only be achieved by illustrators who have acquired skill in free draughtmanship allied with technical craftsmanship.

To digress—Italy is once again setting standards and has recently produced a wealth of good design combined with utility. The Olivetti typewriters, the Vespas and Lambrettas, and the Pinin Farina-styled cars, have brought a new elegance into offices and to the roads. This proves that it is perfectly possible to reconcile the utility of the 'sixties with good design standards. Of course inherent good taste has much to do with it and the acceptance of the fact that good design is good business.

Illustrations 41 and 43 are reproduced by permission of the Standard-Triumph Group. Ltd The author has in the digression above referred to the key-man, the artist designer, who conceives the

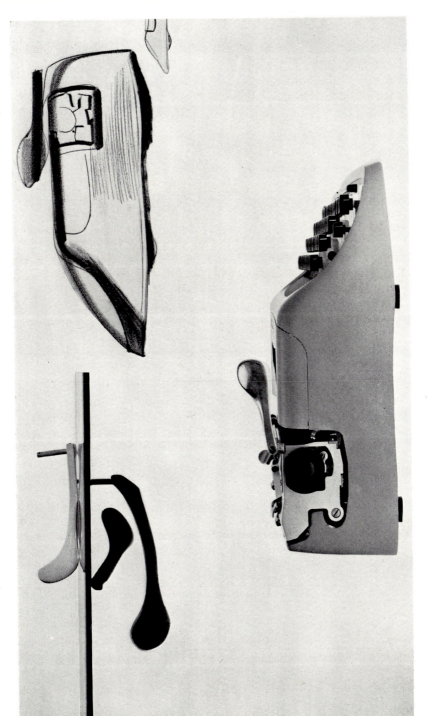

39 British Olivetti Ltd. Olivetti *Studio 44* from sketch to model

40 Ford Motor Company Ltd. Esquisse for frontal treatment of car

41 Standard Triumph Group. Esquisse for a commercial vehicle—perspective

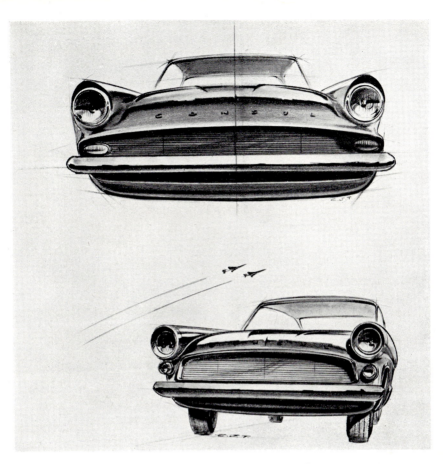

42 Ford Motor Company Ltd. Esquisse for frontal treatment of car

43 Standard Triumph Group. Esquisse for a saloon car—perspective

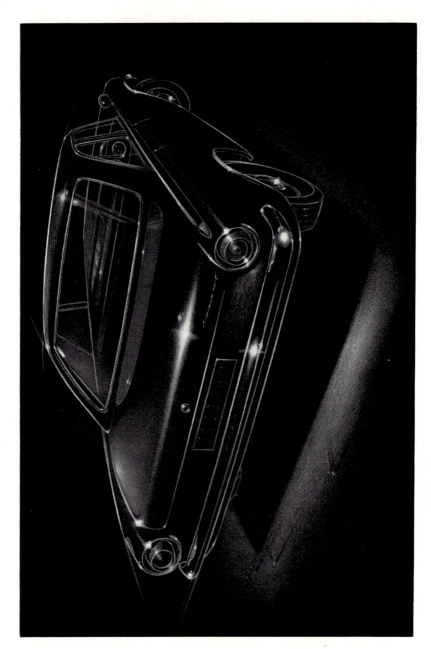

44 Ford Motor Company Ltd. Developed esquisse for new model

original idea drawing from his imagination and experience. In all probability the first tentative thoughts are in the form of 'doodles' which in due course are developed as 'esquisses' (architects' and industrial designers' professional idiom for sketches) and he will consign many of them, before he is satisfied with one or two as a basis for discussion, to the wastepaper basket. During the process of evolution the chosen one is developed into an attractively rendered black and white or coloured perspective drawing, correct in proportion and detail, for further discussion and consideration. In many cases, orthographic drawings in line, giving overall dimensions, will be made to support the artist's impressions.

Illustrations 41 and 43, esquisses for advanced designs for a commercial vehicle and a saloon car respectively, are relatively large drawings 24″ long. Both have been drawn, spontaneously and slickly, with the brush and Chinese ink, by an artist in the styling department. They are by nature transient in character and often only provide a basis for discussion.

Illustration 45 is by courtesy of the Ford Motor Company Ltd, Dagenham. This free perspective in penmanship and wash is prestige illustration. It was widely used in the national press and reproduced remarkably well. It announced the completion of their new Paint, Trim and Assembly Building at Dagenham. This clever free-expression perspective gives a very good idea of the latest plant.

Technical Illustrating: D

TECHNIQUE/CRAFTSMANSHIP

The author has in his book *Trade Draughtsmanship* (p. 42, Three-Dimensional Volumes and Graphic Rendering), fully explained the importance of the illustrator, artist and draughtsman, developing 'volume consciousness' and 'space consciousness', by a complete mastery of basic three-dimensional precision geometrical forms—and in addition, the acquiring of skills (i.e. technique/craftsmanship) to render faithfully in various media these geometrical volumes.

It is of paramount importance to the technical illustrator to have a thorough understanding of three-dimensional geometry as practically every device invented by the human brain and made by humans is an example of applied geometry. Technical draughtsmanship demands both technical and engineering 'honesty' from the illustrator.

The five regular and the three irregular polyhedra can be reduced to a relatively simple scheme of rendered tones, i.e. high-light, half-tone and shadow suffice in themselves to give three-dimensional form to

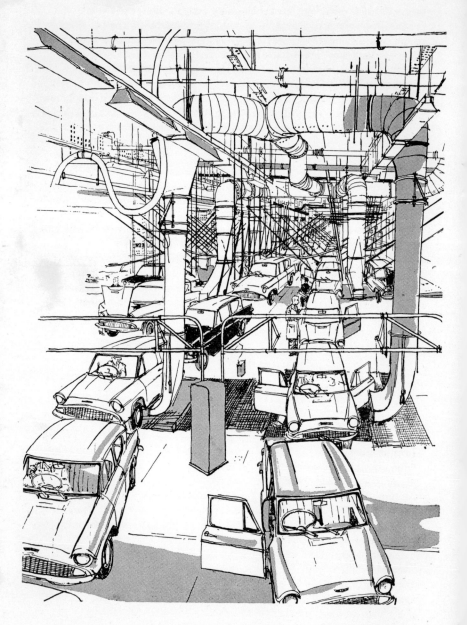

45 Ford Motor Company Ltd. Free perspective prestige illustration

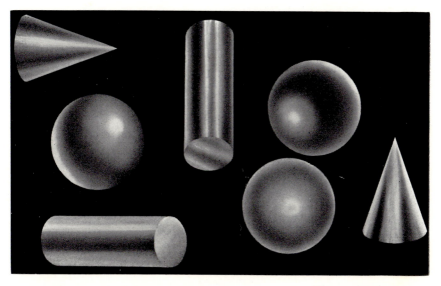

46 Kingston School of Art. Basic study in airbrush technique

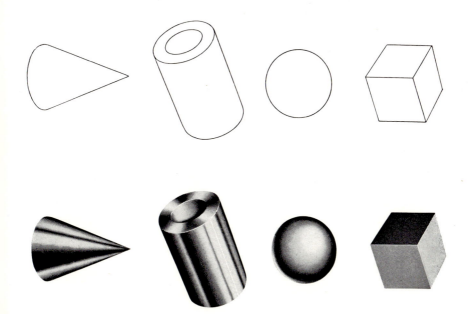

47 A.E.C. Ltd. Technical Illustrating School. Basic study
in airbrush technique

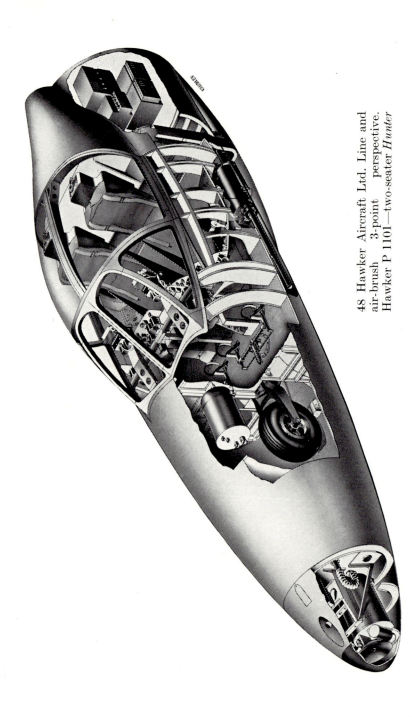

48 Hawker Aircraft Ltd. Line and
air-brush   3-point   perspective.
Hawker P 1101—two-seater *Hunter*

these solids. The round volumes, cone, cylinder, sphere and derivatives, are somewhat more complex to render graphically in view of their roundness. Illustrations 46 and 47 prove that reduced to essentials, i.e. high-light, shadow and three half-tones (lighter half-tone, half-tone and darker half-tone), a convincing rendering is possible whether the surface is a highly polished one or a matt surface. All the basic machine components such as nuts, bolts, bearings, valves, rings, plates, pins, bushes, springs, washers, gear wheels—the list is endless—are geometric in form, assuming when seen in perspective, ellipses, which are possibly the most widely used geometric form in technical illustrating for engineering purposes.

Illustration 46 is by courtesy of Principal Reginald Brill of the Kingston School of Art, Kingston-upon-Thames, and was drawn by a student of technical illustration in the Graphic Art Department. Occasionally drawings are produced on black paper and it is instructive to compare this basic study on ½-imperial sheet with the very accomplished sketch design for a car produced in the Styling Department of the Ford Motor Company Ltd (Illustration 44).

Illustration 47 is by permission of A.E.C. Ltd, Southall, Middlesex, and shows rendered and line drawings on a ¼-imperial sheet of photographic paper, executed by a first year airbrush student in the school of technical illustration within the organisation of A.E.C. Ltd. Such exercises are of the greatest value as these four 'great primary forms' as Le Corbusier calls the cube, sphere and cylinder and cone, are the recurring forms in the technological age in which we live. Similar exercises are advised for all the other techniques and media discussed in this section of the book.

I Line Drawing Techniques

The Use and Limitations of Line to describe the Form of Solid Objects

For reasons of economy a black ink line drawing, sometimes shaded with mechanical tints (screening) is preferred to half-tone drawing which will not reproduce satisfactorily unless one is sure that the paper it is to be printed on will take it. (A rough surfaced printing paper is more suitable for wash drawing.) Large reductions, particularly in line, are not recommended as the illustrator has difficulty in visualising the finished drawing, especially the thickness line—even with the aid of a reducing glass.

In our Introduction we mentioned an attempt which is being made to standardise the presentation of technical information in the aircraft industry. This, of course, includes the standard and format of illustrations. The proposed scheme has been prepared for the Air Transport

63

Association of America. The following extracts from the recommendations are very apposite in this study of line drawing techniques for illustrated parts of catalogues and maintenance manuals:

'*Use of Color*. Because of cost, color shall be used only where absolutely necessary to clarify complicated functional operations. Techniques such as shading, cross-hatching, screening or similar means shall be used in preference. When color is used, the primary colors (red, yellow and blue) or complements thereof (green, purple and orange) are preferable.'

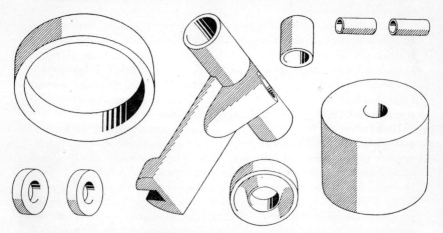

49 Imperial Chemical Industries Ltd. Line drawing of nylon mouldings and monofilament

'*Acceptable and Unacceptable Types*. Acceptable types of illustrations are illustrated and explained in the sample pages preceding. The line drawing is the most desirable type for general use.' (The following are the samples: fig. 2 Outline Drawing; fig. 3 Phantom View; fig. 4 Schematic; fig. 5 Exploded View; fig. 6 Cut-away drawing and fig. 7 Pictorial View with the caption 'Photographs are less desirable than line drawings. They should be used only as a last resort.')

'Particularly undesirable are half-tone and combination line and half-tone illustrations. The manufacturer shall not furnish master copy under any circumstances in the form of brown-line prints, photostats or blue prints.'

'*Call Outs*. Arrowheads on lead lines are optional except where dimensions are indicated.'

The author is of the opinion that in due course manuals dealing with wiring diagrams, structural repairs, illustrated parts and overhaul will inevitably be standardised in the major industries.

Illustrations 49 and 50 are reproduced by courtesy of Imperial Chemical Industries Ltd, Plastics Division. They are taken from the publication *The Properties of I.C.I. Plastics* with illustrations by Walter Greaves. It is an admirable example of lay-out and beautifully drawn line illustration.

Illustration 49 represents some of the uses of nylon mouldings and monofilament. Illustration 50 shows two uses of *Diakon*. These typical drawings in pure line and black shadow with half-tone suggested by closely drawn parallel lines prove that an illustrator of originality is able to produce very personal work even if the forms are as basic as

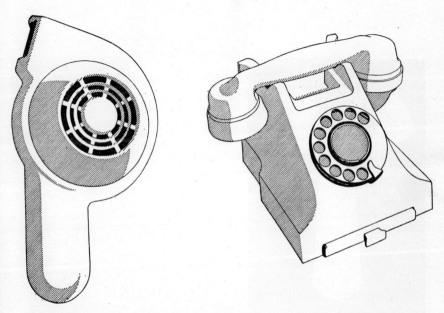

50 Imperial Chemical Industries Ltd. Line drawing showing two uses of *Diakon*

in illustrations 46 and 47. Technical illustrating always calls for three-dimensional interpretation and an appearance of actuality. In all these illustrations the illustrator had the choice of applying mechanical tints (screening) or ruling parallel lines to represent the half-tones. In the author's opinion the artist has chosen wisely.

Illustration 51 is reproduced by permission of Ideal Boilers and Radiators Ltd. The use of pure line in technical illustrating is well exemplified in this illustration which is one of a series appearing in the technical and professional press advertising *Standard* vitreous china. The *Standard Kingston* lavatory basin in perspective with a solid black background is well contrasted with the plan and elevation and their two different half-tone background screenings. The illustrator has produced a striking illustration of this very good design with the absolute minimum of means. In this case the artist has wisely chosen screening for his backgrounds.

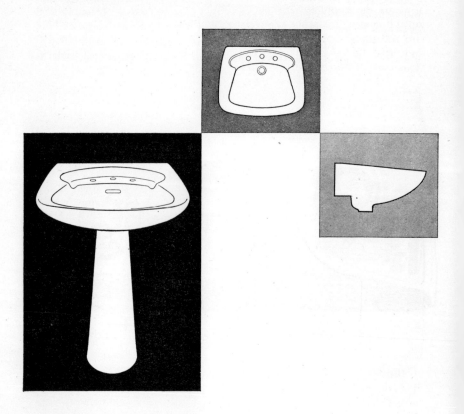

51 Ideal Boilers and Radiators Ltd. Line drawing of *Standard Kingston* lavatory basin

Illustration 52 is by courtesy of British Olivetti Ltd and shows a beautifully drawn *Olivetti Lettera 22* in parallel perspective which is a detail from a technical press advertisement by G. Pintori. The illustrator employs the simplest technique in an able manner by using a sensitive line drawing plus the addition of solid black. He has produced a fine illustration of this distinctive and elegant portable typewriter by an international firm with a world-wide reputation for fine design in its products, its factories and showrooms, its sales publicity and its instruction literature.

Illustration 62 is reproduced by courtesy of A.E.C. Limited, Southall, Middlesex. This is the *Westinghouse* Air Reservoir and Unloader Valve. It is instructive to note that this was drawn from orthographic prints and rendered from knowledge. Also study the lines 'fading out' towards the high-light, by the technique of thinning down each line until it ceases altogether to suggest roundness. The ends of the cylinder are adequately rendered by ruling vertical lines and shadows are indicated by cross-hatching. The block used was fine line letterpress. This type of illustration is excellent for technical literature.

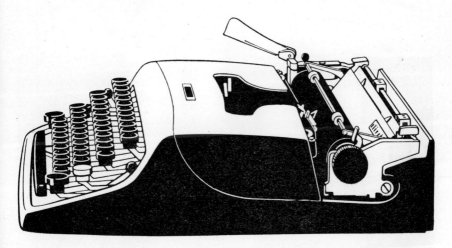

52 British Olivetti Ltd. Line drawing of the *Olivetti Lettera 22*

Illustration 61 is also reproduced by permission of A.E.C. Limited. This illustration of exploded components is technically called a bleach-out. This artwork was originally a photograph of the components—see Illustration 65—the outlines and diagrammatic inked in, and then the photo image was bleached out. The individual components were mounted in relative positions prior to photographing as explained in reference to Illustration 66. The method employed to print their service manuals is fine line block from original artwork $\frac{1}{3}$ larger than finished block size.

Illustration 53 by courtesy of the Ford Motor Company Ltd. This exploded view of Exhauster is an admirable perspective line drawing prepared from blue prints and/or photographs with type-set caption. Block, fine line zinc or magnesium. This drawing is another perfect example of line technique. Note the methods used to differentiate

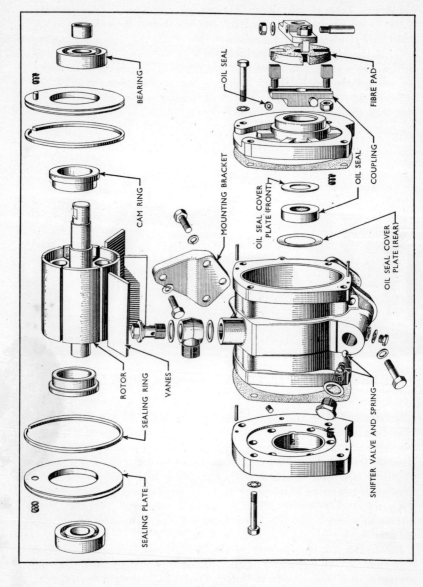

BEARING

OIL SEAL

FIBRE PAD

CAM RING

MOUNTING BRACKET

OIL SEAL COVER PLATE (FRONT)

OIL SEAL

COUPLING

OIL SEAL COVER PLATE (REAR)

ROTOR

SEALING RING

VANES

SEALING PLATE

SNIFTER VALVE AND SPRING

53 Ford Motor Company Ltd. Exploded line perspective from blue prints of exhauster

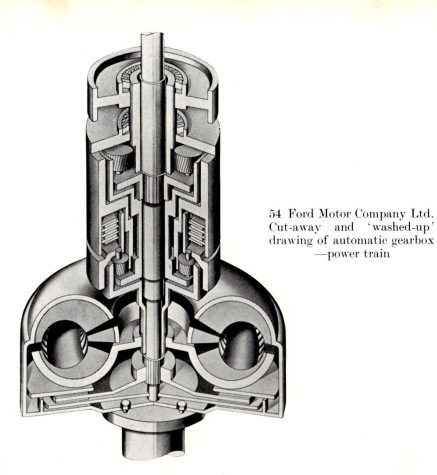

54 Ford Motor Company Ltd.
Cut-away and 'washed-up'
drawing of automatic gearbox
—power train

55 Vauxhall Motors Ltd. Cut-away perspective of *Bedford C A* van

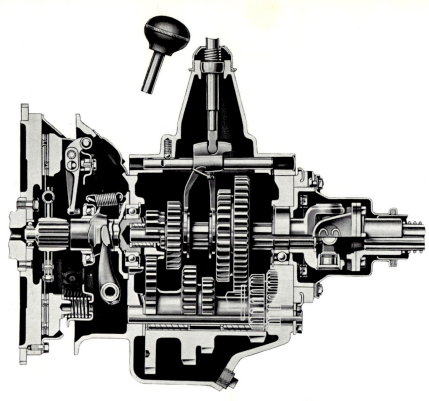

56 Ford Motor Company Ltd. Cut-away and 'washed-up' elevation
of *V8* gearbox

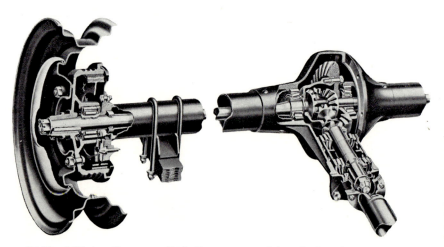

57 Ford Motor Company Ltd. Cut-away and 'washed-up' perspective
of rear axle of *Anglia* and *Prefect*

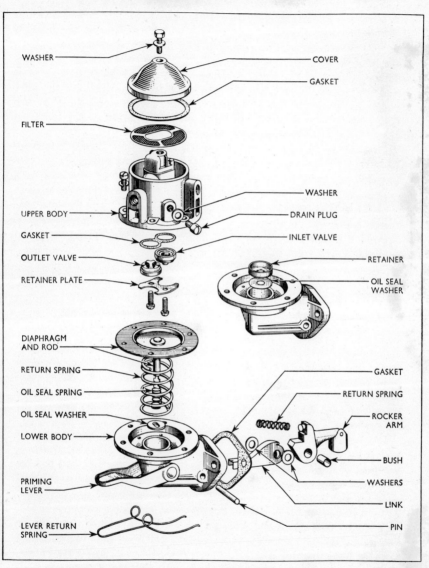

WASHER

COVER

GASKET

FILTER

WASHER

DRAIN PLUG

UPPER BODY

GASKET

INLET VALVE

OUTLET VALVE

RETAINER

RETAINER PLATE

OIL SEAL WASHER

DIAPHRAGM AND ROD

GASKET

RETURN SPRING

RETURN SPRING

OIL SEAL SPRING

ROCKER ARM

OIL SEAL WASHER

LOWER BODY

BUSH

PRIMING LEVER

WASHERS

LINK

LEVER RETURN SPRING

PIN

58 Ford Motor Company Ltd. Exploded line perspective from blue
prints of *V8* fuel pump

materials and metal finishes and particularly the subtleties of one tone merging into the next. For instance, a rough cast surface, fibre, etc., is generally represented by fine dots, close together, fading away or developing into near black according to the position of the light; a bright cylindrical surface, as in Illustration 58, is represented by a series of parallel lines close together or further apart, again according to the position of the light; sometimes domed or semicircular surfaces and medium surfaces lying between the highly polished and the very rough, are rendered by fine lines concentric with the ellipses. Note also the obvious—the rendering of the high-light/shadow on the inside of the cylinder is on the opposite side to that on the outside.

Illustration 58 is also by permission of the Ford Motor Company Ltd of the *V8* fuel pump exploded, and is another excellent perspective line drawing prepared from blue prints and/or photographs and with type-set captions. The annotation in this example is worthy of emulation —as far as it is possible the arrangement of the words is symmetrical which gives the drawing a balanced square look. Undoubtedly a printed type such as Monotype Gill Sans is admirable for technical drawings on account of its clarity.

2 Methods of Tonal Representation

(a) Light and shade in Line and Wash, professionally called 'Washed-up'

A half-tone, or wash drawing, as it is sometimes called, may be derived from the blue prints of individual components or from assembly blue prints, or from a photograph or line drawing or a combination of the latter two means. The process of producing illustrations of this character calls for a very high degree of expertness on the part of the illustrator.

Illustration 54 is by courtesy of the Ford Motor Company Ltd and is an Automatic Gear-Box-Power Train. This cutaway sectional perspective line drawing is prepared from blue prints, 'washed up' for half-tone reproduction with line overlays prepared to represent the 3 solid colours. Blocks originally used were one combined line/half-tone, 120 screen copper block—three fine line zinc blocks for colour printing.

Note: In this particular instance an alternative method would be to prepare finished artwork as a coloured half-tone drawing and then to print from a set of four colour combined line and half-tone blocks. (Refer to next sub section which deals with the use of colour in tone drawing.) This relatively simple example is first rate.

Illustration 56 by courtesy of the Ford Motor Company Ltd, shows the sectional view of the *V8* gearbox which is admirably demonstrated in this cutaway sectional elevation drawing prepared from blue prints

59 Standard Triumph Group. Cut-away and 'washed-up' perspective of *Vanguard* rear-axle

60 Rolls-Royce Ltd. Monochrome from colour cut-away of Rolls-Royce *Avon* turbo-jet

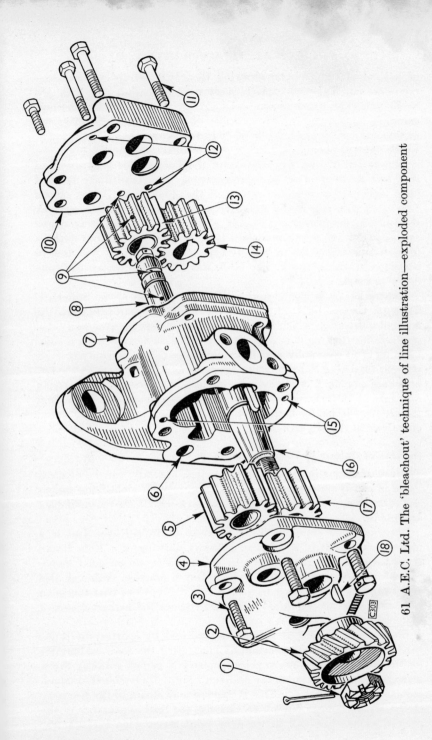

61 A.E.C. Ltd. The 'bleachout' technique of line illustration—exploded component

75

of individual components—drawing then 'washed-up' for half-tone reproduction. Type-set caption sheet used in conjunction with artwork. (In some cases similar drawings are produced from sectional assembly blue prints.) This example of a drawing made plain flat sectional is a form which is obviously less expensive than Illustration 57 which follows. This block was 133 screen copper half-tone.

Illustration 57 also by courtesy of the Ford Motor Company Ltd is a *tour de force* of tonal representation. This beautifully finished fully rendered perspective drawing of the *Anglia* and *Prefect* (1953–1959) rear axle is a model worth very careful study. It is a cutaway sectional drawing developed from blue prints of individual components, and as in the two previous illustrations, 'washed-up' without outlines for half-tone reproduction. Finally type-set caption sheet was used in conjunction with artwork. The block was 133 screen copper half-tone in the original.

Illustration 59 is reproduced with the permission of the Standard-Triumph Group, England. This is the *Vanguard* rear axle from the original illustration which is more than 24″ in length. This half-tone, or wash drawing, as it is alternatively called, is derived from a combination of photography and line draughtsmanship. Technically both straight rendering in body colour (*gouache*) and rendering with the airbrush are combined on a photographic base. The process of preparing illustrations for technical purposes demands the greatest accuracy from the artists. Blocks: for half-tone this organisation called for 120 screen on copper in the original.

(b) Use of Colour in Tone Drawing

The use of colour in explanatory drawings generally can be of great value in clarifying cutaway sectioned drawings, in identifying metals and other basic materials, or component parts used in the more complex assemblies.

Illustration 60 reproduced by courtesy of Rolls-Royce Ltd is a monochrome print of a coloured cutaway drawing of a Rolls-Royce *Avon* turbo jet. It is necessary to use filters to obtain good monochrome from colour, and this is Rolls-Royce practice. Although this is not reproduced in colour in this volume it is obvious that this is an extraordinarily accomplished work and reaches the highest standard of technical illustrating.

Illustrations 63 and 64 are also reproduced by courtesy of Rolls-Royce Ltd. The first Illustration 63 illustrating the *Solex* carburetter for the Rolls-Royce *B* range petrol engine is a perfect cutaway three-point perspective drawn on the grid and beautifully rendered in monochrome with the airbrush. This is conclusive evidence of the necessity of the artist training himself to visualise the final appearance of the project whilst it is still in the blue print stage. This artwork was produced by the illustrator from the original orthographic projections. The Illustration 64 of the two-stage centrifugal compressor of the Rolls-Royce *Dart* prop. jet is a further accomplished work drawn as in the previous example. In this instance note the annotation arranged in such a way as to give the drawing a square look. Rolls-Royce's practice is to use letterpress type—direct on line drawings—and on to overlays for half-tone. *Letraset* is also used occasionally. The following notes on their illustrators' methods are very instructive.

(a) All have been produced from 'blues' (as prints are always called) and photographic information confined to *outside* of casings and main units only.

(b) The airbrush is used habitually for all tonal work.

(c) All perspective drawings in line and tone are produced on the grid.

(d) Original: photo litho offset throughout. Contact screens and deep etch for half-tone.

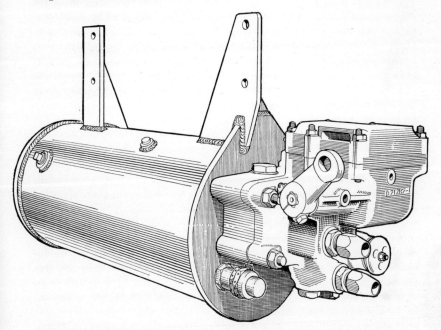

62 A.E.C. Ltd. Line rendering from orthographic blue prints of *Westinghouse* Air Reservoir and Unloader Valve

Printing Methods Employed by A.E.C. The two methods most widely used are dealt with in detail, namely photo litho and letterpress. The method employed to print their service manuals is letterpress 120 screen in the case of half-tone and fine line in the case of line block. They have found that in preparing artwork, the best results are obtained by having the original artwork $\frac{1}{3}$ larger than finished block size. They do not recommend large reductions particularly in line as the illustrator has difficulty in visualising the finished drawing, especially the thickness of line.

(c) Creative Use of the Airbrush and Retouching

The airbrush has an indispensable place in technical art and to realise its unlimited possibilities in purely creative work it is of great importance that the artist has complete mastery of the instrument. The correct pressure to use for general retouching is 30 lb. per square inch but for very intricate work a lower pressure is required. Basic exercises in airbrushing, such as those shown in Illustrations 46 and 47 should be undertaken by every student who aspires to be a technical illustrator. Airbrushed drawings and photographs must not be carried to undesirable extremes as fine creative photography, such as the Olivetti Illustrations 37 and 39 conclusively prove. But as is so often the case in engineering works of the magnitude of many of the contributors to this work, the photographer has to deal with components that have not been prepared and may have an undesirable background.

Illustration 65 by courtesy of A.E.C. Limited is the actual untouched photograph from the same negative as Illustration 61 on which the artwork was inked in and the photo image bleached out. This exploded view of components mounted in their relative positions is virtually a new technique and was employed also in Illustration 66 of an exploded view of water pumps by permission of the Ford Motor Company Ltd. This is a photograph of individual components mounted in their relative positions and retouched with the airbrush to delete mounting material and generally to improve subject matter. It was completed with type-set captions. The original block, 133 screen copper half-tone. From the purely technical angle this demonstrates in a striking manner a justifiable use of the airbrush.

A brief study of the technique of photographing exploded assemblies on the thread and rod principle is worthy of inclusion. Apart from the need of a great deal of patience and ingenuity, one of the most difficult aspects of photographing exploded components has been to obtain a true horizontal centre line throughout the diameter of the coaxially aligned units. Briefly, nylon thread with spreaders is added to the transparent rod method of suspension. These act as a straining force between the components, thereby allowing each to be adjusted individually for a horizontal datum line. This technique is possible even for an exploded engine, which requires some twenty shots of assemblies each one on the thread and rod method of suspension and support, to complete the composite print which is then photo-copied. Finally, retouching and airbrushing results in an illustration in which all the

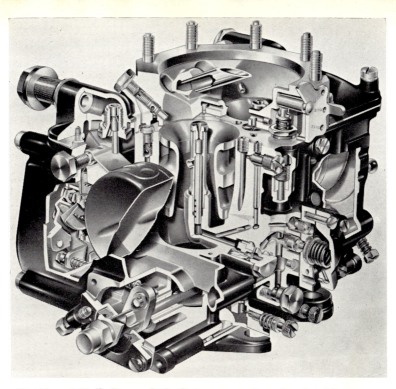

63 (Above) Rolls-Royce Ltd. Cut-away and rendered grid perspective of *Solex* carburetter; 64 cut-away, rendered and annotated illustration of *Dart* propeller jet

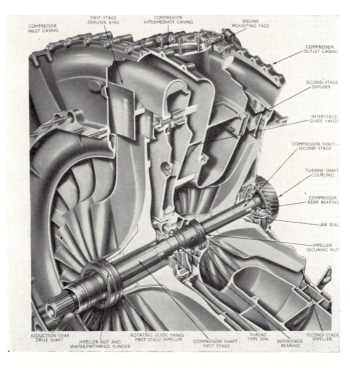

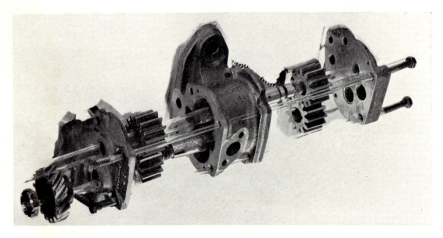

65 A.E.C. Ltd. Exploded assembly on the thread and rod principle

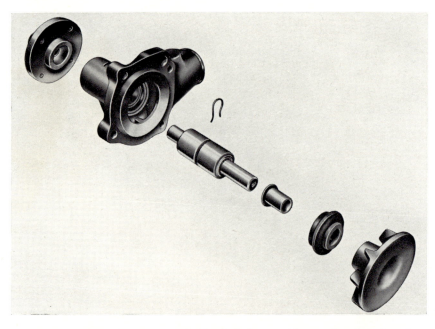

66 Ford Motor Company Ltd. Exploded assembly on the thread and rod principle, but retouched airbrush work to delete mounting material

visible signs of component support are removed by airbrush technique similar to Illustration 66 (by courtesy of the Ford Motor Co. Ltd).

Illustration 48 was produced in the technical publications department of Hawker Aircraft Ltd by whose courtesy it is reproduced. This line and airbrush drawing 22″ long of a Hawker *P 1101*—two-seater Hunter —Front Fuselage is a perfect three-point cut-away perspective rendering by Mr Chidley who is their chief illustrator, and who is also a visiting teacher of technical illustration at Kingston School of Art. This ably executed work proves beyond doubt that the airbrush rightly and skilfully handled is as capable of producing purely creative artwork as any other medium. The student will find it very instructive and helpful to compare this drawing with Illustration 11 from the same technical publications department, which is a black and white line drawing of the front fuselage of the same aeroplane, differing only in the detail cut-away. Scholarly sympathetic interpretations, full of life, with emphasis where required, are demonstrable in both techniques used by the illustrators. Among twenty-three illustrations in this work employing airbrush technique the reader is advised to study its possibilities by carefully examining the following illustrations: 14, 19, 21, 28, 29, 35, 36, 46, 47, 48, 54, 55, 56, 57, 59, 60, 63, 64, 66, 82, 83, 85 and 86. The last three are particularly impressive by displaying both an architectural and engineering application.

(d) Mechanical Tints and their Application

Mechanical tints are universally used today for both shading and back-grounds in support of line drawing. They can be very attractive and are often preferred to half-tone renderings, chiefly for reasons of economy. These mechanical tone screens are manufactured in the United States of America and are marketed by agents in this country under trade names, i.e. *Zip-A-Tone* and *Craftints*. *Zip-A-Tone* is a quick and easy screen to apply to the drawing for reproduction. Place the screen over parts of the drawing to be shaded; then rub over the screen with a piece of paper, about the size and thickness of a blotter, held beneath the tips of the fingers—starting from the bottom of the screen and rubbing from left to right, moving upward as the screen adheres to the drawing. Now cut and strip away parts not wanted— then go over the screen again as described above, using sufficient pressure to cause the screen to adhere thoroughly tight to the drawing. Now all is ready for the engraver.

With the cutting needle one can cut away portions of *Zip-A-Tone* screens much easier than with a knife or any other cutting instrument. You cut with the cutting needle just as easily as though you were using a pen and you do not have to turn the needle between your fingers as you cut around corners, etc., as you naturally would have to do should you be using a knife.

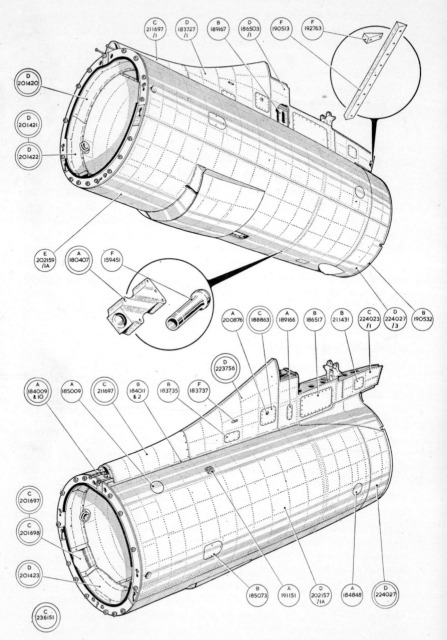

67 Directorate General of Equipment. Air Ministry. Rear fuselage, two-seater *Hunter*. Mechanical screen technique. *Crown Copyright*

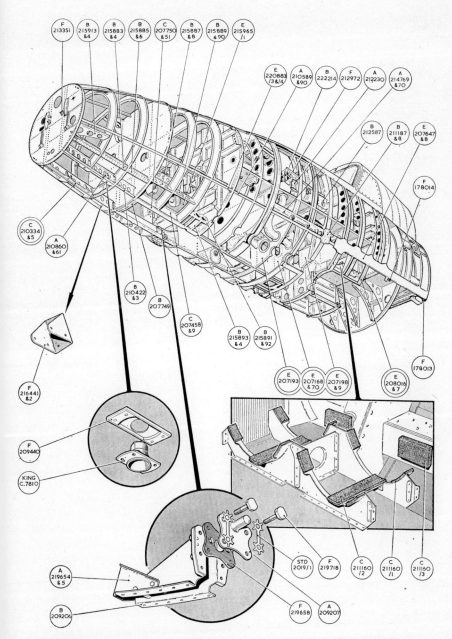

68 Directorate General of Equipment, Air Ministry. Front fuselage,
two-seater *Hunter*. Mechanical screen technique. *Crown Copyright*

83

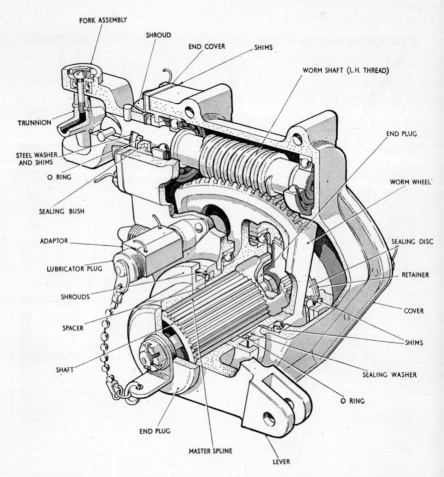

FORK ASSEMBLY

SHROUD

END COVER

SHIMS

WORM SHAFT (L.H. THREAD)

TRUNNION

END PLUG

STEEL WASHER AND SHIMS

O RING

WORM WHEEL

SEALING BUSH

ADAPTOR

SEALING DISC

LUBRICATOR PLUG

RETAINER

SHROUDS

COVER

SPACER

SHIMS

SHAFT

SEALING WASHER

O RING

END PLUG

MASTER SPLINE

LEVER

69 Bristol Aircraft Ltd. Component with mechanical screen technique

Zip-A-Tone leaves no adhesive on the drawing. Fifty-one screens are available in the $16\frac{3}{4}'' \times 21\frac{3}{4}''$ size and come in positive and reverse. It adheres firmly to the drawing. Should it be desired to have the screen adhere permanently to the drawing, then go over the screen with a bone burnisher using pressure, but only after the cutting and stripping has been executed.

70 A.E.I. Lamp & Lighting Co. Ltd. Perspective view of shop interior lighting rendered with screens

In selecting a screen for $\frac{1}{2}$-reduction or $\frac{1}{3}$-reduction you will have to select one that will reduce to the desired tone. There is a range of screens which are used to break up solid blacks and will reduce, if required, as those just described.

Illustrations 67 and 68. Permission to reproduce these plates is granted by the Directorate General of Equipment, Air Ministry. Both are from official volumes and were produced by technical artists in the technical publications department of Hawker Aircraft Ltd and they demonstrate very ably the possibilities of mechanical screens rightly used. Illustration 87 is the rear fuselage of a two-seater *Hunter* and shows a mechanical screen used to suggest the cylindrical form in a simple and restrained way. Illustration 68 showing the front fuselage, with enlarged details, has screens used primarily as backgrounds whilst the method of detailing certain components is admirably done. This illustration is also valuable as an example of three-point perspective looking upwards. The method of annotation in both drawings is most satisfactory, helping to give them a squared-up appearance.

71 A.E.I. Lamp & Lighting Co. Ltd. Perspective view of ship's cabin rendered with screens

Illustrations 69 and 72 are by courtesy of Bristol Aircraft Ltd. The first is of a cut-away perspective of a component clearly demonstrating the newer technique of using mechanical tints for shading, whilst the second shows the use of the traditional methods of shading. Both illustrations employ the excellent technique of line emphasis where necessary.

Illustrations 70 showing shop interior lighting, and 71 design for a cabin in a liner, are reproduced by permission of the A.E.I. Lamp & Lighting Company Ltd and the latter exhibits a free-perspective interior view. It is drawn freely in black and white, but instead of using various line techniques to represent the half-tones, mechanical tints have been employed with commendable results. It will be appreciated that this technique is most suitable for technical booklets, etc. Also the illustrator can spare himself tedious ruling and dotting and produce work quicker by the use of mechanical tints.

Ten illustrations used throughout this work exhibit the use of these screens. Readers are advised to study Illustrations 12, 30, 32, 51, 67, 68, 69, 70, 71 and 79, the latter being a perfect example of *Zip-A-Tone* screen technique.

3 Annotation

Style of Lettering and Mechanical Aids

Illustration 73 is Crown copyright reproduced with the permission of the Controller of H.M. Stationery Office. This plate is an example from an official volume, with type-set annotation arranged, as far as possible, so as to give the illustration a squared-up appearance. This is an excellent line drawing which is the most desirable type for general use, of hood locking and jettison details with lubrication of a *Hawker Pilot* two-seater, produced in the technical publications department of Hawker Aircraft Ltd, Kingston-upon-Thames.

(a) No better model for both alphabets and numerals, for any type of drawing or illustration for any industry, is available than the well-known *Gill Sans* designed by Eric Gill for the Monotype Company. Unfortunately this has either to be drawn by hand or printed, therefore in many organisations, in view of the time factor involved, the quicker mechanical expedient is employed.

(b) *Letraset*, a type transfer system, is successful for either technical illustrations or working drawings. In a simple operation letters from a specially printed type sheet can be transferred direct to any art surface *without* transfer film or background—the ink alone is carried, and the completed work looks just as though set in type and printed. A carrier frame and a selection of type sheets from an impeccably finished range, large enough for practically any purpose, is available. These are arranged in font system giving most of the letters in most frequent use. The letters are sharp, opaque and self-adhering to any art surface.

(c) *Artype* is similar to the mechanical screens and applied directly to the layout or finished artwork. The characters are printed on the underside of transparent self-adhering acetate sheets and are very simply transfered to any smooth surface. The necessity for setting type or hand-lettering is eliminated, as each character is easily removed from the sheet with a stylus and applied with light pressure only.

(d) Finally, the well-known *Uno* stencils are available. They comprise complete alphabets, numerals and technical symbols accurately cut in firmly mounted sheets of thin but tough blue transparent plastic. *Uno* pens fit neatly into the guides provided, thus drawing lines of proper thickness at a single stroke, facilitating the execution of well-drawn letters, numerals, etc.

Thirty-two illustrations used throughout this treatise show the use of various systems of lettering and annotations. The student is strongly advised to study Illustrations 1, 2, 5, 12, 23, 25, 26, 27, 38, 53, 58, 61, 64, 67, 68, 73, 77, 84 and 86. The numbering in certain illustrations is 'round the clock' which affords rapid location and identification of the components. This is a vital factor particularly where a large number of items or components are involved.

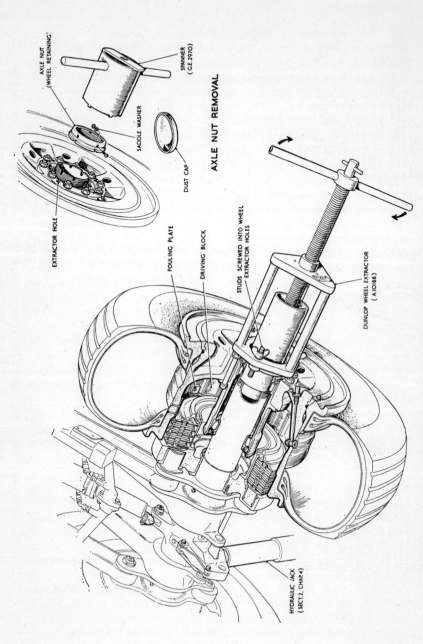

AXLE NUT (WHEEL RETAINING)

SPANNER (GE.2970)

SADDLE WASHER

DUST CAP

EXTRACTOR HOLE

AXLE NUT REMOVAL

FOULING PLATE

DRIVING BLOCK

STUDS SCREWED INTO WHEEL EXTRACTOR HOLES

DUNLOP WHEEL EXTRACTOR (A.101188)

HYDRAULIC JACK (SECT.2, CHAP.4)

72 Bristol Aircraft Ltd. Component rendered in the traditional pen and ink technique

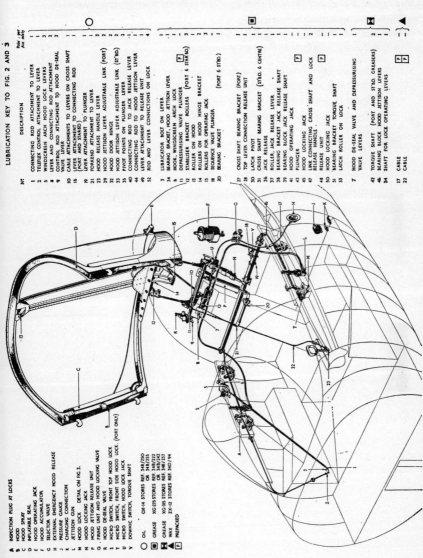

LUBRICATION KEY TO FIG. 2 AND 3

N°	DESCRIPTION	Pair per Air entry
1	CONNECTING ROD ATTACHMENT TO LEVER	3
2	TELEFLEX CONTROL ATTACHMENT TO LEVER	5
8	WINDSCREEN ARCH HOOD LOCK LEVERS	2
4	LEVER AND CONNECTING ROD ATTACHMENT	2
9	CONTROL ROD ATTACHMENT TO HOOD DE-SEAL VALVE LEVER	2
10	CABLE ATTACHMENTS TO LEVERS ON CROSS SHAFT	4
16	LEVER ATTACHMENT TO CONNECTING ROD (PORT AND STAR'BD)	2
21	LEVER ATTACHMENT TO PLUNGER	2
23	FOREHAND ATTACHMENT TO LEVER	2
33	HOOD RELEASE HANDLE LEVER	2
29	HOOD JETTISON LEVER ADJUSTABLE LINK (PORT)	2
32	HOOD DOOR HINGE	2
35	HOOD JETTISON LEVER ADJUSTABLE LINK (STB'D)	2
40	PIVOT POINTS ON PLUNGER LEVER RELEASE LEVER	2
45	CONNECTING ROD TO JACK RELEASE LEVER	2
52	CONNECTING ROD TO HOOD JETTISON LEVER	4
49	LEVER ATTACHMENT TO RELEASE UNIT	
52	ROD AND LEVER CONNECTIONS ON LOCK	
3	LUBRICATOR BOLT ON LEVER	3
34	BEARING BRACKET, HOOD JETTISON LEVER	2
6	HOOK, WINDSCREEN ARCH LOCK	2
—	DEPRESSURISING VALVE PLUNGER	
13	STABILISER BRACKET ROLLERS (PORT & STAR'BD)	2
14	ROLLER ON HOOD HINGE BRACKET	2
15	ROLLERS ON HOOD HINGE BRACKET	2
18	ROLLERS FOR OPERATING JACK	1
19	SEQUENCE VALVE PLUNGER	1
20	BEARING BRACKET (PORT & STB'D.)	2
27	CROSS SHAFT BEARING BRACKET (PORT)	1
28	TOP LEVER CONNECTION RELEASE UNIT	1
30	LATCH PIVOT	1
31	CROSS SHAFT BEARING BRACKET (STB'D. & CENTRE)	2
36	JACK RELEASE	1
37	ROLLER, JACK RELEASE LEVER	1
38	BEARING BRACKET JACK RELEASE SHAFT	1
39	BEARING BLOCK JACK RELEASE SHAFT	
41	HOOD OPERATING JACK	2
—	PLUNGER	
44	HOOD LOCKING JACK	2
47	LINK CONNECTING CROSS SHAFT AND LOCK	
48	RELEASE HANDLE	
—	RELEASE UNIT	
50	HOOD LOCKING JACK	1
51	BEARING BRACKET TORQUE SHAFT	1
53	LATCH ROLLER ON LOCK	
42	TORQUE SHAFT (PORT AND STB'D. GREASERS)	2
46	BEARING BLOCK HOOD JETTISON LEVERS	1
54	SHAFT FOR LOCK OPERATING LEVERS	
17	CABLE	
22	CABLE	

INSPECTION PLUG AT LOCKS

- A — INSPECTION PLUG AT LOCKS
- B — HOOD
- C — INFLATABLE SEAL
- D — HOOD SPRAY
- E — HOOD OPERATING JACK
- F — HOOD ACCUMULATOR
- G — SELECTOR VALVE
- H — EXTERNAL EMERGENCY HOOD RELEASE
- J — PRESSURE GAUGE
- K — CHARGING CONNECTION
- L — JETTISON GUN
- M — HOOD LOCK. DETAIL ON FIG.1.
- N — HOOD LOCKING JACK
- P — HOOD JETTISON RELEASE UNIT
- Q — FIRING UNIT AND HOOD LOCKING VALVE
- R — HOOD DE-SEAL VALVE
- S — MICRO SWITCH, FRONT TOP HOOD LOCK
- T — MICRO SWITCH, FRONT SIDE HOOD LOCK. (PORT ONLY)
- U — MICRO SWITCH, HOOD LOCK JACK
- V — DOWNLOC SWITCH, TORQUE SHAFT

- ○ OIL — OX-14 STORES REF. 34B/750 OR 34B/255
- ☐ GREASE — XG-275 STORES REF. 34B/212 OR 34B/249
- ✖ GREASE — XG-35 STORES REF. 34B/737
- ▲ WAX — ZX-12 STORES REF. 34D/94
- ◣ PREPACKED

73 H.M. Stationery Office. Annotated line drawing of detail of *Hawker P 1101* two-seater.
Crown Copyright

89

On the other hand some compilers of parts catalogues will claim that it is easier to number associated components numerically. The reader can judge for himself by comparing illustrations employing alternative methods of annotated numbering.

Annotations on the actual illustrations should be avoided wherever possible because it always raises two problems:

(i) Inconsistency in sizes of annotations due to differing reduction of the artwork to block size and while this would not apply in any one illustration it spoils the appearance of the layout of the publication if inconsistencies are apparent on adjacent illustrations.

(ii) It may not be necessary to point out the obvious disadvantages of stencilling or printing annotations on the artwork when the publication is subject to translation.

Instead of annotations on drawings the illustrator should specify type-set overlays.

SECTION 3

Action Examples and Case Histories

All the examples in this section and the preceding sections are of great value as they give the reader a very good insight into the professional *standard* required in industry.

How will this work and/or how will this look are questions constantly being asked by all who are concerned with function and design. The answer can be given in several ways including by word or by diagram or other illustration; after all, how better can the answer be given than in pictorial form which even solves language difficulties.

Every major industry and certain professions adopt their own special method of graphic explanation and their choice depends upon the type of intelligence they wish to impart to others, as the preceding sections of this work have demonstrated. For instance, architects employ axonometric projection and two-point perspective—on the other hand the engineering illustrator, particularly in the aeronautical and automobile industries, invariably uses three-point perspective.

That technical illustrators are employed by the Admiralty and at the Harwell Research Establishment may at first seem rather odd. But when it is realised that information which has been obtained by individual research must be handed on for use by others, this fact appears quite normal. The work undertaken by illustrators at the Admiralty is varied and covers a wide scope but nevertheless it follows the general lines of technical illustration done elsewhere. The author is unable to show illustration work by the Admiralty Technical Illustrator Pools, but permission has been granted by the United Kingdom Atomic Energy Authority for typical examples of their work to be reproduced in this section plus observations by Mr Gibbons, UKAEA Chief Illustrator.

The sequence of 'live' examples which follows these observations shows in action the power and scope of this virtually new profession and the very important and ever-growing part it plays in the life of the community. The preceding sections of this work explain fully how to master the pictorial means of communicating intelligence and the exacting qualities of draughtsmanship necessary so as to acquire the skills and discipline to produce work of a comparable high standard of professionalism.

To Sum Up: Many of these technical illustrations—some previews— were produced from general assembly drawings of engineering, still

91

on the drawing board or in the early stages of construction. Advance information of new products loses much of its value if it is not accompanied by fully-informative technical illustrations having a technical completeness for advance selling of the project to men with a technical and aesthetic background. Technical illustration is extensively used throughout the engineering industries for such purposes as the advance illustration of aeroplanes, motorcars, light engineering consumer goods, engines, gearboxes, generators and machine tools generally. From fully-dimensioned orthographic engineering drawings, drawings are built up on one of the geometric grids of three-dimensional perspective or in isometric projection, as explained earlier in this book. Examples are given of explanatory technical illustrations which show the complete general view of the machine or product in full detail, i.e. the cut-away perspective view to reveal method of operation, etc., the exploded and partially cut-away view and the fully exploded view in which the components are co-axially aligned.

The ultimate goal in design for mass-production is the creation of type forms for standardisation for such diverse products as refrigerators and units for pre-fabrication in building, for aeroplanes and commercial vehicles. These would meet all the technical and aesthetic demands as well as commercial requirements of today, i.e. eliminate every drawback of machine production without sacrificing any of its real advantages. The word standardisation is one which is apt to engender a certain amount of alarm. It is associated with sameness, monotony, even a 'robot' society. But as many of our technical illustrators prove, the right way to use standardisation represents opportunity for the designer—not limitations. For example, look at objects as dissimilar as the *Britannia* aircraft and the *Olivetti* typewriter. Standards have always existed—the conscious adoption of type-forms—as a criterion throughout history, e.g. the Greek classic of Athens or the Regency elegance of Cheltenham or Bath.

The beauty of first-class engineering is presented in this sequence of illustrations of the 'works' which display interesting features of industrial and/or mechanical design.

Illustrations 75 and 76 are reproduced by courtesy of Bristol Aircraft Ltd. The first of the *Britannia 300* is the finalised drawing shown first in its process of development in Illustration 13. This illustration is first class and shows how new and interesting forms are evolved for reasons which are mainly functional. The second is a very remarkable and accomplished cut-away three-point perspective projection of the *Britannia 310*, produced on the *Mavitta 3 D Drawing Board*. In the beautiful interior of this aeroplane a considerable degree of comfort, space and light has been attained in a much more difficult sphere than that of the ordinary house which is so ill-planned as a general rule. The quality of penmanship is magnificent—note particularly the quality

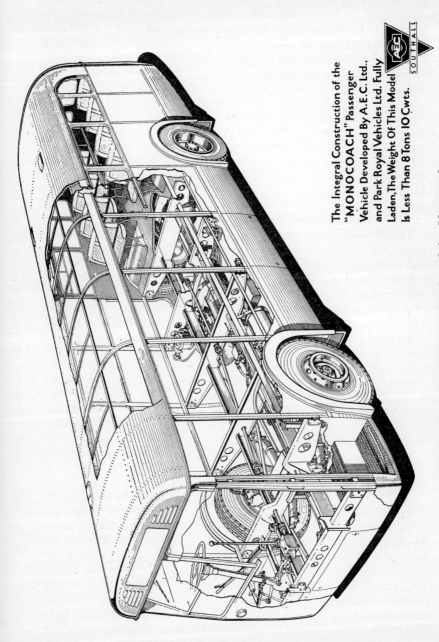

The Integral Construction of the "MONOCOACH" Passenger Vehicle Developed By A.E.C. Ltd., and Park Royal Vehicles Ltd. Fully Laden, The Weight Of This Model Is Less Than 8 Tons 10 Cwts.

74 A.E.C. Ltd. Cut-away perspective of the *Monocoach*

93

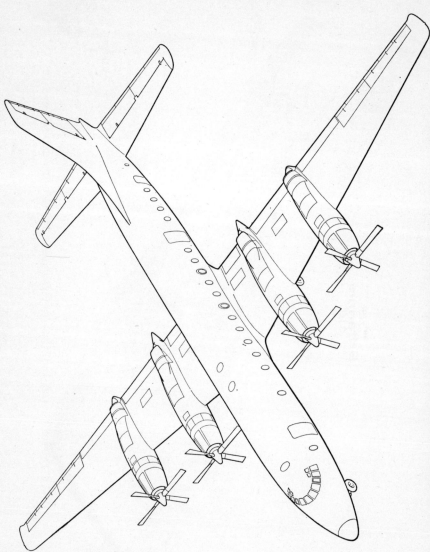

75 Bristol Aircraft Ltd. *Britannia 300 produced on Mavitta 3 D Drawing Board*

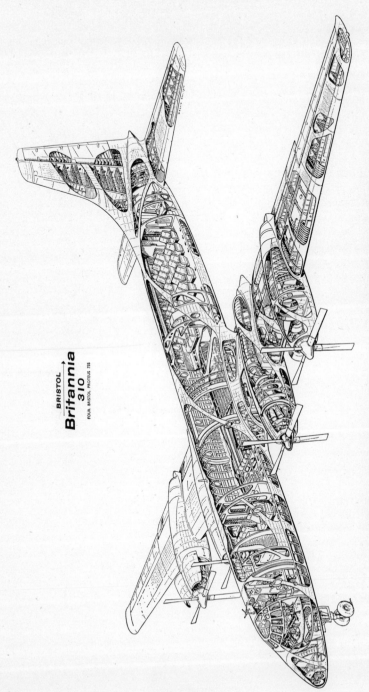

BRISTOL
Britannia
310

FOUR BRISTOL PROTEUS 755

76 Bristol Aircraft Ltd. Cut-away *Britannia 310. Mavitta 3 D perspective*

95

of line and emphasis to bring forms forward and conversely where necessary the delicacy of line where recession is called for.

Illustration 55 is by courtesy of Vauxhall Motors Ltd. This is the *Bedford CA Van* showing double-skin body side panels. This brilliant cut-away perspective is drawn partly from photographs and partly from blue prints, then 'washed-up' in colour. Note that a monochrome version was photo-copied from the colour original. The following is the technical data originally used: Letterpress—block, 4-colour set or monochrome, 133 screen copper cut-out. In both cases used with or without type-set overlay. This has also been reproduced by offset litho.

Illustration 74 reproduced by permission of A.E.C. Limited, Southall. This extremely able and informative black and white drawing of the *Monocoach* is a model of its kind. This illustration from a production point of view represents another approach to the problem. In this case the illustration was prepared from a similar photograph of a chassis from which the perspective was scaled off and enlarged to 16″ left to right. The modifications were then made in the pencil stage, the body outline added and finally inked in.

Illustration 82 reproduction by courtesy of Fairey Aviation Ltd, showing most attractively the *Fairey Rotodyne*—the world's first vertical take-off airliner—this cut-away perspective drawing exhibits in a scholarly, dramatic manner the complete Rotodyne. The technique employed in the production of this beautiful illustration was another departure from accepted practice. This was a photographic print, 19″ × 13″, of the original ink-line drawing, rendered in colour with the airbrush. This illustration and Illustration 48 of the *Hawker P 1101*—two-seater *Hunter*—front fuselage, in the author's opinion, show the use of the airbrush in a creative way.

Illustration 77 is reproduced by courtesy of Bristol Aircraft Ltd and shows the undercarriage extended and bogie in landing position. This perspective drawing is a fine example of penmanship. The line and dot shading is beautifully and expressively executed—it would be difficult to find a finer illustration as an example of black and white work. The diagram showing the undercarriage retracted, extending and extended leaves nothing to be desired and the annotation throughout is excellent.

Illustration 78 by courtesy of British Motor Corporation Ltd (The Austin Motor Company Ltd, Birmingham, England). This perspective illustration in line is in the book of consolidated technical data for the *Austin Seven 850* (which is the twin of the *Mini-Minor*). This model was conceived by Mr Alec Issigonis, resident chief designer and is among the finest examples of European small car design. It has simplicity in line and form and the more a design can be produced which appears to be free from effort the more beautiful it generally is. This line drawing, and Illustrations 17 and 18, strikingly convey this to the

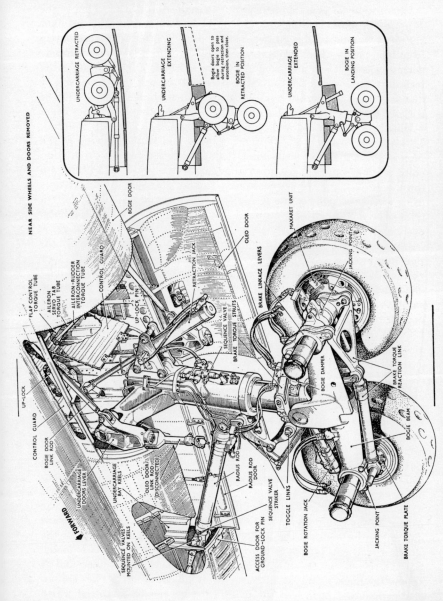

NEAR SIDE WHEELS AND DOORS REMOVED

UNDERCARRIAGE RETRACTED

UNDERCARRIAGE EXTENDING

Bogie doors open to allow bogie to pass during retraction and extension, then close.

BOGIE IN RETRACTED POSITION

UNDERCARRIAGE EXTENDED

BOGIE IN LANDING POSITION

BOGIE DOOR

OLEO DOOR

RETRACTION JACK

CONTROL GUARD

UP-LOCK PIN

FLAP CONTROL TORQUE TUBE

AILERON SERVO TAB TORQUE TUBE

AILERON-RUDDER INTERCONNECTION TORQUE TUBE

SEQUENCE VALVE

BRAKE TORQUE STRUTS

BRAKE LINKAGE LEVERS

MAXARET UNIT

JACKING POINT

CONTROL GUARD

UP-LOCK

BOGIE DAMPER

BRAKE TORQUE REACTION LINK

FORWARD

BOGIE DOOR LINK ROD

UNDERCARRIAGE BAY KEELS

OLEO DOOR LINK ROD (DISCONNECTED)

RADIUS ROD

SEQUENCE VALVE STRIKER

TOGGLE LINKS

BOGIE BEAM

UNDERCARRIAGE DOORS LEVER

SEQUENCE VALVES MOUNTED ON KEELS

ACCESS DOOR FOR GROUND-LOCK PIN

BOGIE ROTATION JACK

JACKING POINT

BRAKE TORQUE PLATE

77 Bristol Aircraft Ltd. Perspective and diagram of undercarriage and bogie

97

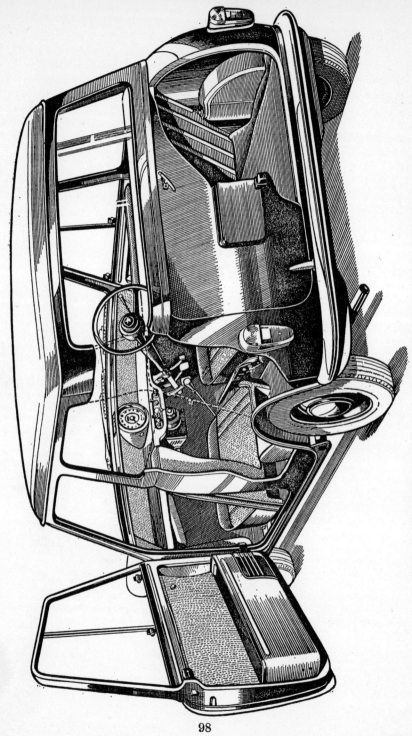

78 British Motor Corporation Ltd. Perspective of the *Austin Seven 850*

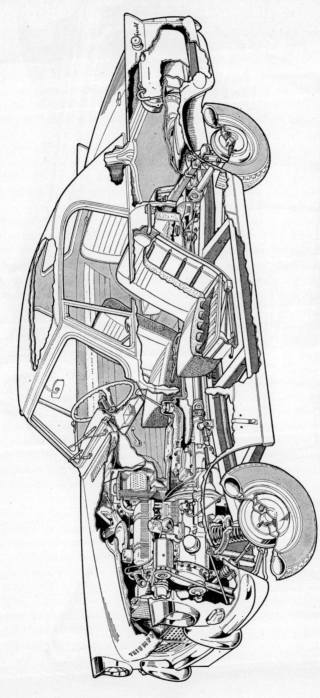

79 Standard-Triumph Group, Coventry. Cut-away perspective of Standard-Triumph *Herald*

spectator. The rendering has strength and vigour and the whole range of tones from white to black is excellent.

Illustration 79 is reproduced by courtesy of the Standard-Triumph Group, Coventry. The Italians have proved themselves to be masters of style in car design and their influence continues and even shows signs of increasing. Giovanni Michelotti of Turin played a part in the development of the Standard-Triumph *Herald* shown in this very fine cut-away perspective view.

Tracings made from photographs have a special place in the world of technical illustrations, provided the lens and camera are suitable for the work envisaged; perspective may be added without distortion. In the case of this cut-away sectioned *Herald* car, the basic illustration was provided by double exposure. The car in question had been prepared for exhibition work. It had, in fact been cut in half. The vehicle was jacked up and the near-side wheels removed. The car was then photographed, the wheels re-fitted and photographed again without moving the camera or the car. In this way a composite photograph was produced. The tracing was then made and panels were then added and cut away and components brought into prominence to produce the illustration. Finally the major areas are shaded by using *Zip-A-Tone* mechanical tints which, incidentally, is the most satisfactory treatment for an illustration of this type. It is interesting and instructive to note that the Standard-Triumph Group illustrators do not use the *Mavitta 3 D Drawing Board* or the perspective grids, but rely on the other methods which have been described.

Illustrations 80 and 81 are illustrated by kind permission of The Kleine Company Ltd, London. Apart from the subject matter these two cut-away perspective drawings in line display characteristics different from any others which have been analysed. First—architects' two-point perspective has been used by the illustrator—i.e. vertical lines in reality are drawn vertically in the illustration. This was undoubtedly the right choice, as no apparent distortion is noticeable. Secondly, the rendering of these two views respectively of 80 floor and 81 ceiling, is very simple, i.e. white for high-light, black for strong shadow, and half-tones of dots, lines and cross-hatch. Both are strikingly successful and the annotation is particularly good. They appeared in professional literature and they also have a very professional air about them.

Illustration 86 by courtesy of Marconi's Wireless Telegraph Company Ltd. This is an 'exploded' view, in line only, of the backplate and junction box assembly *Type 3021* VHF Transmitter type *AD 305* which is from the illustrated parts list compiled to assist owners and operators to order any spare part component they may require for servicing the type *AD 305* equipment. This list contains sixteen 'exploded' illustrations of the major units of this transmitter and Illustration 86 is a typical example. The following method is used to prepare drawings:

Hollow Tile Floor or Roof: bearing on Internal Encased Steelwork

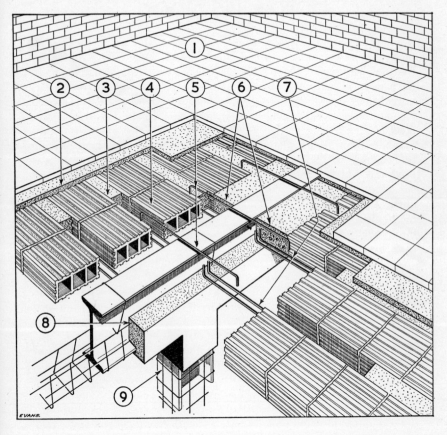

80 The Kleine Company Ltd. Architect's cut-away perspective view of floor

1. Prepare pencil rough on tracing paper (using a model twice final size).
2. Transfer to art board—or trace on linen.
3. Ink-in using *Pelicon* drawing ink, brush, ellipse guides, french curves and usual drawing equipment.
4. Thicken lines where necessary, add shadows and scrape high lights.

Incorporation of Heating Panels
in soffit of
Hollow Tile Floor

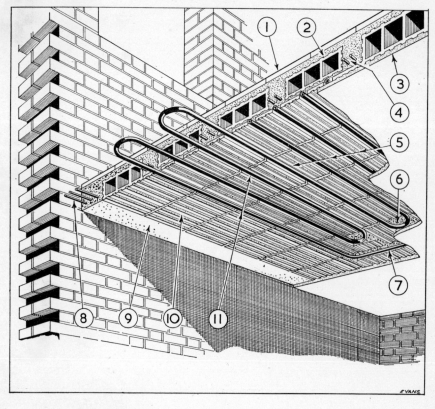

81 The Kleine Company Ltd. Architect's cut-away perspective view
of ceiling

5. Stencil notes and balloon numbers.

The following method is used to reproduce drawings:

1. Photographically reduce 2:1 and develop negative.
2. Prepare photo-sensitised aluminium rotaplate.
3. Ink and print.

Note: The black areas with white stencilling in part of a block

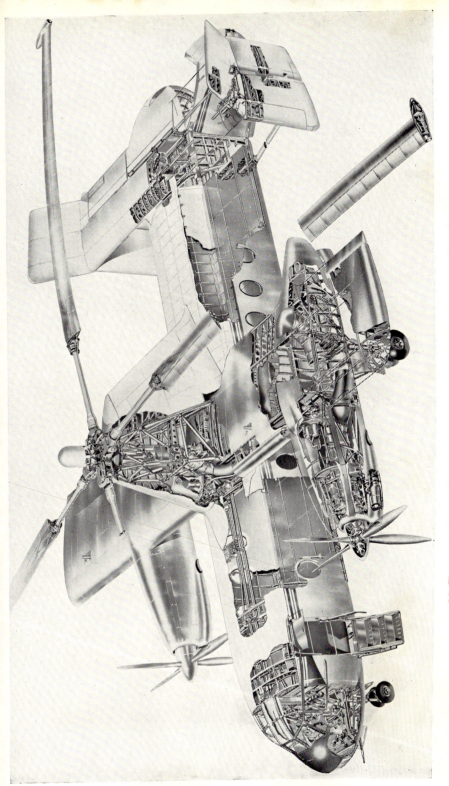

82 Fairey Aviation Ltd. Cut-away perspective of the Fairey *Rotodyne*

83 United Kingdom Atomic Energy Authority. Cut-away perspective of reactor *Zenith*

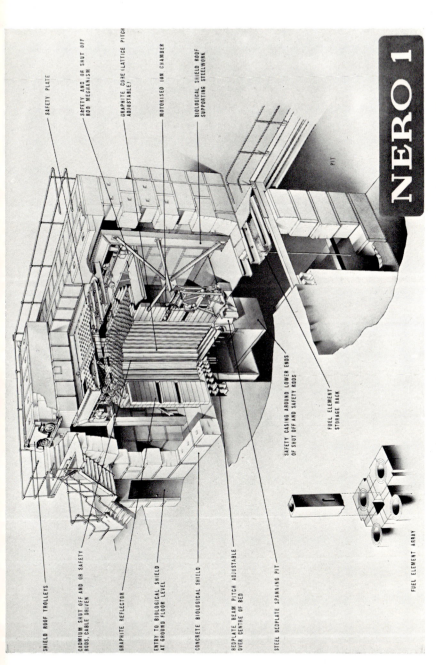

SAFETY PLATE

SAFETY AND OR SHUT OFF ROD MECHANISM

GRAPHITE CORE (LATTICE PITCH ADJUSTABLE)

MOTORISED ION CHAMBER

BIOLOGICAL SHIELD ROOF SUPPORTING STEELWORK

PIT

NERO 1

SHIELD ROOF TROLLEYS

CADMIUM SHUT OFF AND OR SAFETY RODS, CABLE DRIVEN

GRAPHITE REFLECTOR

ENTRY TO BIOLOGICAL SHIELD AT GROUND FLOOR LEVEL

CONCRETE BIOLOGICAL SHIELD

BEDPLATE BEAM PITCH ADJUSTABLE OVER CENTRE OF BED

STEEL BEDPLATE SPANNING PIT

SAFETY CASING AROUND LOWER ENDS OF SHUT OFF AND SAFETY RODS

FUEL ELEMENT STORAGE RACK

FUEL ELEMENT ARRAY

84 United Kingdom Atomic Energy Authority. Cut-away 3-point perspective of reactor *Nero 1*

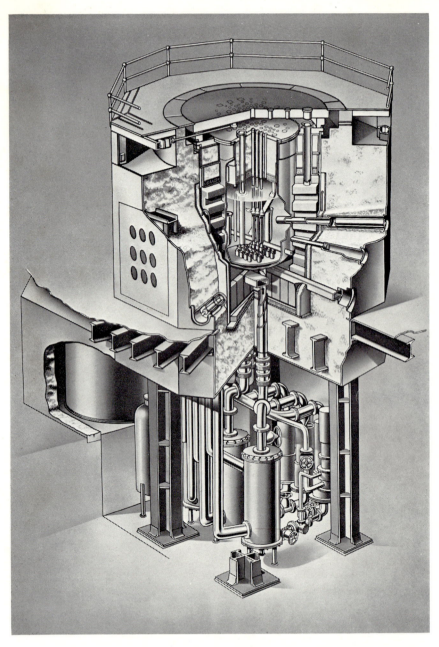

85 United Kingdom Atomic Energy Authority. Cut-away perspective
of reactor *Dido*

schematic diagram (Illustration 38) are prepared by a photo-reversal method.

Illustrations 83, 84 and 85 are reproduced by permission of the United Kingdom Atomic Energy Authority. These three drawings of reactors were drawn before the construction of the equipment and in general this is usual at Harwell in the illustration section.

Illustration 83, *Zenith* zero energy high temperature gas-cooled reactor. This is a brilliant example of the 'cut-away' technique. This illustration and the two which follow demanded both technical and architectural knowledge on the part of the illustrators and represent a unique combination of skills.

The *Zenith* illustration began as a pencil drawing to aid senior design staff at discussions. A tone drawing was airbrushed by the artist and copies used by site engineers as a means of communication with the numerous contractors. The final drawing (with insets not shown here for reasons of space) was used both as a display diagram and also as the basis of a publicity handout. The scale/size of the reactor has been cleverly suggested by the personnel.

Illustration 84, *Nero 1* reactor. This cut-away drawing in three-point perspective was used both as a display diagram and a scientific report illustration. The original drawing was projected from machine drawings prior to the erection of the reactor; it was airbrushed in monotone. The annotation in this exemplar 'squares-up' the illustration.

Illustration 85, *Dido*—a heavy water reactor under construction at Harwell. It will be used for testing the materials to be used in future reactors for producing power. Its function in research on the production of nuclear power can be compared with the rôle of the wind tunnel in aerodynamic research.

The *Dido* illustration again was made prior to construction. It was first displayed as a colour 'cut-away' diagram at the Geneva Atoms for Peace Conference 1955. Later other insets were added and it was used as a wall diagram. It has also been used in reports as a half-tone. Another exacting 'cut-away' problem for the illustrator.

An Artist's Job at Harwell, with acknowledgments to Mr Gerard Gibbons of the Atomic Energy Research Establishment:

The workings of an atomic research establishment call for much graphic explanation and the skilful artist is fully employed in describing visually the intricacies of plant layout and equipment. Gerard Gibbons, senior illustrator, here explains this task, which calls for meticulous draughtsmanship and technical knowledge. The artists, or illustrators, at Harwell produce work under three main headings:

First—Illustration for Instruction Manuals. The Electronics Division at Harwell designs a variety of instruments for detecting and measuring radio-activity. These instruments are produced in large numbers and used throughout the world. With each instrument is included an

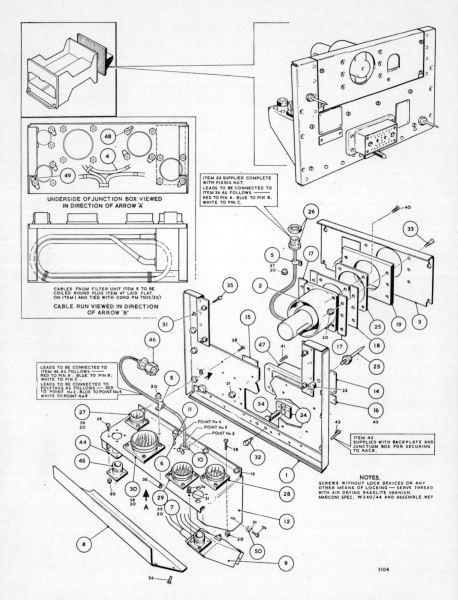

UNDERSIDE OF JUNCTION BOX VIEWED
IN DIRECTION OF ARROW 'A'

ITEM 26 SUPPLIED COMPLETE
WITH FIXING NUT.
LEADS TO BE CONNECTED TO
ITEM 26 AS FOLLOWS —
RED TO PIN A . BLUE TO PIN B.
WHITE TO PIN C.

CABLES FROM FILTER UNIT ITEM 9 TO BE
COILED ROUND PLUG ITEM 47 LAID FLAT
ON ITEM 1 AND TIED WITH CORD PM 7505/23/1

CABLE RUN VIEWED IN DIRECTION
OF ARROW 'B'

LEADS TO BE CONNECTED TO
ITEM 46 AS FOLLOWS —
RED TO PIN A . BLUE TO PIN B.
WHITE TO PIN C .
LEADS TO BE CONNECTED TO
POLYTAGS AS FOLLOWS — RED
TO POINT No 2. BLUE TO POINT No 6
WHITE TO POINT No 9

POINT No 6
POINT No 9
POINT No 2

ITEM 42
SUPPLIED WITH BACKPLATE AND
JUNCTION BOX FOR SECURING
TO RACK.

NOTES.
SCREWS WITHOUT LOCK DEVICES OR ANY
OTHER MEANS OF LOCKING — SERVE THREAD
WITH AIR DRYING BAKELITE VARNISH.
MARCONI SPEC. W240/44 AND ASSEMBLE WET

1104

86 Marconi's Wireless Telegraph Company Ltd. Exploded view of unit
of transmitter *AD 305*

108

instruction handbook which gives complete information on the design, circuits and use of the equipment. Graphs, waveforms, view of the instrument and other illustrations are placed in the text. The books are printed by offset litho; line rather than half-tone is used for economy, mechanical tints are used for both shading and backgrounds. In the Maintenance chapter must be included the tabulation of all components with reference to the stylised layout of the circuit diagram. The overriding consideration in preparing these illustrations is to present information clearly.

Second—This work is akin to the technical illustration used in the motor and aircraft industries where 'exploded' and 'cut-away' drawings are produced mainly from orthographic machine drawings. They are used to illustrate Atomic Energy Research Establishment Reports. These reports describe in detail the work done by scientists and engineers on experimental or theoretical research. If the equipment is made of metal it is more convenient to prepare sketches than to section and photograph the parts of interest; sometimes equipment is radio-active and cannot be viewed under normal conditions. These reports are also printed offset litho and the accent again is on complete and accurate information. Illustration can be a direct aid to research. Alterations to the research facilities in a reactor under construction may be suggested. To visualise the difficulties this may cause in such a complicated project from a multitude of orthographic design drawings is no mean task; numerous headaches and explanations are avoided and time saved by preparing an accurate 'cut-away' drawing showing the reactor in detail.

Third—The Atomic Energy Authority has made use of illustrative displays publicly and within the Atomic Energy Research Establishment. The use of clear illustrations ensures that the visitor is presented with facts in a readily understandable form. The successful United Kingdom Section of the Atomic Energy Exhibition in Geneva utilised where necessary the art of the technical illustrator. Accurate 'cutaway' drawings supported excellent models and photographs.

At Harwell technical art is being utilised as one of the many aids to Atomic Energy Research and the work produced has a high standard of finish, which can only be achieved by illustrators who have acquired skill in technical craftsmanship.

The foregoing case-history of the Illustration Section of the Atomic Energy Research Establishment, Harwell, and of several others in the preceding sections, gives a comprehensive picture of the important part the technical illustrator can play today in industry. These case-histories present also the fundamental requirements for the exponents of this interesting and, at the same time, exacting profession.